# MELANOMA 20

# A collection of Patient Stories

Our mission is to drive ADVOCACY including making skin checks more affordable for Australians, EDUCATE our future generations on how to prevent melanoma and non melanoma skin cancer, fund RESEARCH via clinical trials and provide SUPPORT so no one goes alone on the melanoma and non-melanoma skin cancer journey.

https://www.australianskincancerfoundation.org/

# MELANOMA 28

## A collection of 28 Patient Stories

## Melanoma in the lives of ordinary Australians

*edited by Jay Allen OAM & Aileen Eiszele*

**TOYOTA**

Proudly supported by Toyota Australia

First published in Australia in 2024 by Jay Allen OAM

https://themelanomaman.com.au/

Copyright © Jay Allen OAM, 2024

ISBN: (paperback) 978-0-6486361-4-4

ISBN: (ebook) 978-0-6486361-5-1

Print production and ebook through eBook Alchemy – www.ebookalchemy.com.au

In association with Clouds of Magellan Press – cloudsofmagellanpress.net

Cover image: The Studio Creative

Design: Gordon Thompson

Production coordination: Andrew Farrell

# Contents

Afterword: writing about heroes ... Aileen Eiszele
Definitions

# About this book

This book is a collection of real-life testimonials from people diagnosed with melanoma. The common link between each is the association with Jay Allen, a survivor of stage 3 melanoma, who accompanied the patients and families depicted within throughout their treatment journeys. Jay's story is the last in the book. He is also the founder of Australian Skin Cancer Foundation.

Through the words of the patients and their family members, these stories tell of the courage, generosity and endurance of people suffering adversity, and how we can achieve more together than apart. The book also highlights the importance of recent treatment breakthroughs and emphasises, from the patient's perspective, how much more needs to be done to improve early diagnosis, ensure the prompt initiation of appropriate treatments, and fund high quality research.

*Content advisory*

In general, the people who conveyed these stories found the exercise helpful and therapeutic. They describe adversity, suffering and death. Reading these stories may cause discomfort, especially to those associated with someone who has been diagnosed with melanoma. We encourage the prospective reader to be conscious of the nature of the content before making the decision to read on.

# Preface

This book is filled with inspiration and heartbreak. For many years while walking across the country raising funds for melanoma research I have constantly been asked about support and why the melanoma and non-melanoma skin cancer journey is lonely and tough. Having worked in the melanoma world for fourteen years it was always something that has been close to my heart. Because I've been there without support. It can be so scary, fearful, and very, very, isolating and lonely.

I felt there were many gaps in the system and many charities being run like a business, but in particular it always came back to lack of support, which is why the Australian Skin Cancer Foundation was born December 2021. We have four pillars:

**Advocacy**
We want to make skin checks free for all Australians

**Education**
We want to educate as many of our future generations as possible

**Research**
We need a cure and will continue funding clinical trials

**Support**
We don't want anyone to go through the skin cancer journey alone.

Many of my friends are featured in this book. It will bring tears to your eyes, and it will bring you hope. It will show you the triumphs and devastation that skin cancer causes to a lot of families across our nation.

It will educate you on why skin cancer is deadly here in Australia and it may save your life by pushing you to get your skin checked.

Melanoma has changed my life. And I will never take any day for granted. But it's brought me to meet some of the most beautiful, inspiring, courageous, humans on earth. And we must continue day in, day out, until this disease is eradicated.

Jay Allen OAM
The Melanoma Man
*jay@themelanomaman.com.au*

# Foreword

*Deb Knight*

Jay, you have not stopped supporting the many diagnosed on their journey ever since this disease struck you at the age of just 32.

From a young truck driver then overnight turned into a survivor and advocate for not just melanoma but also non melanoma skin cancers is something to be commended on. You have organised numerous walks across the country and walked the talk raising awareness and funds for research and walked in trenches with your friends helping bring light in a very dark world for some who sadly are no longer with us.

It doesn't stop there; you continue supporting many families helping them navigate a world without their loved one. While still dealing with your own demons of yearly scans and tests ensuring melanoma doesn't reoccur. You witnessed gaps in the system with support and brought to life support systems not only here in Australia but across the globe. Advocating for patients and their families on their behalf and opened doors to many that may never have had the opportunity to access treatments with some patients still alive today because of your advocacy.

What a privilege to write the foreword for these personal experiences of how strong the human spirit can be, stories of resilience and triumphant stories of hope and sadly the devastating impact that Australia's national cancer melanoma has had on 28 melanoma patients and their families.

*Deborah Knight. Journalist and Australian Skin Cancer foundation ambassador.*

# Giving so that those who come after may have a better life

*Gregory Poche AO & Kay Van Norton Poche AO*

It was just over ten years ago that Greg and his very dear friend, Reg Richardson, made the decision to support research into one of the biggest killers in Australia, melanoma.

Greg had sold his company and was looking to use his financial privilege for the future. Reg had been involved with fundraising, mainly for the arts, but also wanted to help raise funds for projects that had the potential to change the future. Together these two friends went on a mission to reach their goal. They met with top researchers in the field of melanoma and learned that many of these gifted professors, doctors and clinicians had been funding their own research and working in hallways or in whatever place they could find and afford. It was obvious to Greg and Reg that there was immense talent involved and that what researchers needed the most were funds and a dedicated arena to reach their goals. This was the catalyst to create a specialised research institute.

We met Jay through one of his walks in Manly, Sydney, New South Wales. The walks were the brainchild of Jay and his great friend James Economides. James had lost his son to melanoma and wished to turn his grief into action to raise awareness and funds to fight this dreadful disease. Both are such advocates for awareness and education, and we became aware that Jay was a tremendous tool in the fight to wake Australia up to the dangers of sun exposure.

Jay has dedicated his efforts every day as a melanoma survivor to opening hearts and minds to what can be achieved through supporting research and awareness. We became very close as we try each day to achieve our goal to end deaths due to melanoma.

When our donation was first given some ten years ago, both Greg and I understood that we probably would not see the goal achieved in our lifetime, but that was the reality of our 'gift for the future'. As the philanthropic monies can be earmarked for exactly where you would like them to go, they go so much further than one would think. Therefore, we have experienced the joy of seeing the amazing progress that has been made in the field of melanoma research as we push towards the end goal.

It is with joy and humility that we join all the dedicated people from all walks of life who work tirelessly to find the answers to give families, patients, friends, and colleagues the hope that one day we will live without the dreadful loss we have all endured.

Please remember that when we give to the future, we give with the knowledge that those who come after may have a better life. We understand that the foundation of humanity is always based on what we can do to change the circumstances of those in genuine need. It is a true embarrassment of riches to be able to do so.

Thank you so much.

# MELANOMA 28

Ruby Stead

# Ruby Stead

I am passionate about giving back to people who need to hear stories of hope. I was terrified when I was first diagnosed. I received what is normally a terminal diagnosis and I've survived. If I can help just one person who is feeling afraid, then that fills my heart. I also want to help with awareness as this can happen to anyone. I never dreamed it would happen to me ...

I was diagnosed with melanoma at age 41 and I'm now 45 years old. When I was diagnosed, I lived in Bondi, Sydney, but now I live in Canberra with my partner Steve, our 10-year-old son Sonny, and our cats Molly and Bandit. I was a graphic designer prior to my cancer diagnosis. I stopped working when I got sick and haven't returned.

As a family, we love riding bikes together and going on weekend drives to explore the countryside. I love crafts and trying new things. Lately, I've been doing a bit of sewing and learning to make royal icing cookies. My hopes for the future are for us to move north and live in a Queenslander. I want to live a pretty normal life with lots of bits of beauty in it. Normal is so underrated. I can't stress that enough. I would love a life free from the fear of cancer.

My melanoma story began in 2013. I had an in-situ melanoma removed from my back and was given the all-clear, but like any melanoma diagnosis, the rounds of regular check-ups followed. In 2016, another melanoma popped up. This time, it was located on my chest and was classified as stage 2. Once again, after surgery, I was told that I was in the clear and put on a schedule of regular check-ups. In June of 2017, one week before our big move from Canberra to the beachside suburb of Bondi, I felt a lump under my armpit towards the breast. I knew that it was important to keep an eye out for anything unusual or suspicious with my health, and so I immediately had it checked – it was a Sunday. Within the same week, I underwent a scan, which came back as being inconclusive, and then had the lump biopsied. The following Friday, the day before my son's seventh birthday, we moved to Sydney as Steve had secured a new job, and that's when our whole world was tipped upside down.

At seven o'clock in the evening, my doctor called to let me know that the biopsy results had confirmed melanoma, that he was referring me to a melanoma treatment centre, and that I would require scans. I fell to my knees. I was petrified. The next few months were a whirlwind of appointments. This time, I was given a stage 3 diagnosis. There were scans and a big surgery to remove all 37 lymph nodes from my armpit. It was really painful, and I had to have a drain in for five weeks following surgery. Despite everything, having surgery felt like action was being taken and that there was a plan of attack.

Three months later, my cancer had spread to stage 4.

My parents were shell-shocked for a long time and always put on a brave face for me. I would just need to look at Dad and tears would stream down my face. Telling Mum initially was the hardest thing I've had to do. I couldn't speak to my nan for quite some time because all I could do was cry when I heard her voice. My partner was holding us all together as well as trying to maintain his new job in Sydney. My son was a little bit too young to really understand it completely, and through it all he showed us what an amazing, resilient young man he is. Moving homes and going to a whole new school is enough for any young child, but Sonny found himself also enveloped by the fear that surrounded our family. Just looking at him would make me cry and I tried my hardest not to do so in front of him.

I was put on immunotherapy. The plan for me was to receive an initial four intravenous doses of the combination of ipilimumab and nivolumab, commonly known as 'ipi/nivo', followed by a fortnightly infusion of just nivolumab for two years until it became intolerable due to side-effects, or there was disease progression. The goal was to eradicate the disease and then stay on maintenance treatment for two years. I made it through three of the combined treatments which was a feat in itself. It's highly toxic and some people only make it through one or two treatments.

After the first infusion, I developed a cough that didn't let up day or night. After about a week, I had horrendous pain in my side so much so that I thought I'd busted a rib or a muscle from coughing so much. The pain was unbearable, and I felt so sick that I went to hospital. I was scanned in the ER, aware at this point that there were a few melanoma lesions on my liver. The ER doctor came in to deliver the results of the scans and said, without pause or a considerate thought for my darling 7-year-old son who was in the room with us, 'I'm sorry, your lungs are covered, completely covered in melanoma spots – there's too many to count.' There was also some fluid on the lung that was causing a lot of pain. This news was, of course, horrendous. I was hooked up to machines and they all started beeping because I was so scared. All I could think about was how they've just told me this in front of my son. I spent that night in a room on my own thinking my treatment wasn't working and terrified I was going to die.

The next morning, the sun was out. The oncologists were quite cheerful when they came in to see me and reassured me that sometimes the melanoma grows before it dies when it's first hit with treatment. This gave me the hope I needed to carry on. I went on to receive my second treatment, became very sick, and ended up back in hospital with what is known as a 'thyroid storm'. Thyroid problems are a very common problem with immunotherapy treatment, but apparently a thyroid storm is very rare. Mine turned out to be life threatening. When the doctors had balanced out the problems, I received my third infusion, but it was back to hospital again. This time, I was extremely sick, especially with rigors, and I had autoimmune hepatitis. I underwent another scan while I was in hospital and was told that I had clots on my lungs but that at least the melanoma was stable.

I felt like I was in a boxing ring, one blow after the other. I was put on blood thinning injections and had to inject myself twice daily for the next six months. I also started a very high dose of steroids for the liver. It was all horrible and very frightening, but I remained as brave as I could. It slowly sank in that I could focus on the fact that there was 'no new melanoma'. This was another glimmer of hope and gave me a bit more fuel in the tank.

As it was Christmas, I decided to pack us up and drive to Mum's place on the far north coast of New South Wales for Christmas. The steroids gave me a stack of energy and I felt alive and positive. By early January, my liver function had come back, I was weaned off the steroids, and allowed to resume immunotherapy treatment with just nivolumab and not the combination – joy! I continued nivolumab fortnightly, and regular 12-weekly scans showed in March that everything was a bit smaller, and that the treatment was working. However, by June (the week before we'd decided to pack up and move back to Canberra), my stomach pain had become too much, and I was admitted back into hospital. I thought it would be for a quick check-up, but it turned into eight nights. Eventually, I was diagnosed with duodenitis and so I was put back on steroids.

Again, I felt amazing on high dose steroids, although perhaps a bit manic! I only stayed on the high dose for a bit as once you start to lower the dose it is fairly brutal on the moods! We moved back to Canberra but being on steroids meant no treatment because immunotherapy ramps up your immune system (hence autoimmune side-effects) and steroids do the opposite.

I had been on this round of steroids for three months when I felt two new lumps appear, one in the arm and the other in my cheek. I was so scared, and the scans confirmed that the melanoma had recurred. Luckily, there were only these two new spots. Somewhere during this rollercoaster, I'd also found out that the melanoma had spread to some bones, but these deposits were showing up as most likely being 'treated metastases'. Calling upon all my strength during what was another incredibly frightening time, I went back on nivolumab. I received it fortnightly from September 18, 2017 to January 19, 2018 and it worked again. I miraculously felt the lumps in my arm and cheek disappear! However, I felt my stomach starting up again, so my doctor stopped my treatment to save me from potentially having to go back on steroids and back into that vicious cycle.

I have been stable ever since. Scans to this day show that almost all the disease is dead apart from some very low activity in the bone and in one lymph node in the chest. I had a bout of pancreatitis that was treatment induced even eight months after stopping. I have dealt with ongoing fatigue, inflammation and migraines or headaches. It's been tremendously brutal but I'm here to tell the tale.

## Reflections

Being diagnosed with melanoma has tested all of us to the core. The trauma, the fear, the unknown. Then the terror as I faced my own mortality and the thought that I'd failed my family and would now become a burden to them. It's been exhausting in every way, but through it all, I did find hope.

## Hope

I looked for and found hope everywhere. I just had to believe and open my heart and mind to it. It took strength and faith. I found so much hope in hearing success stories. Mum and I read through the success stories on 'The Melanoma Man' Facebook page one afternoon, cheering and crying. I found hope and 'knowing' and true friendship in the eyes of all the fellow patients I met. I found hope when I went out and had an ice cream with my family, when I looked at the ocean, found a feather or a coin, or saw a beautiful sunset or moon rising.

Early in my story, when I was in an Uber with my dear mum on my way to my very first specialist appointment, 'Three Little Birds' by Bob Marley came on the radio. The lyrics, 'Every little thing's gonna be alright', gave me goosebumps. It was as if I was being sent a strong message. Bob Marley ironically died of melanoma, making it even more meaningful. I continued to hear that song at crucial times. My mum encountered a friend who admitted to having been singing the song all day. Then one day, on a bad day (they were fast and furious in those early days!), I got in the car and before I drove off said, 'I just need a sign, please please please, I just need a sign.' I started the car and drove up the road and 'Three Little Birds' came on the radio. There is always hope …

## Support

If you are diagnosed with melanoma or any type of cancer, getting the right support is vital. I joined Jay Allen's 'The Melanoma Man' Facebook page and was following him at the time that I progressed to stage 4. When this diagnosis came through, Jay was there straight away and took Mum and I for a coffee. I am honoured to say that I've been friends with Jay ever since. He has been an incredible support throughout my three-year melanoma journey so far. I'd be lost without him and, as a patient himself, he completely gets it. Through Jay, I've met other incredible people. Bringing people together who are going through the same horrific experience is invaluable. I have spent a lot of time over the last couple of years also giving back as much as I can to other patients. My support group was crucial in my illness and recovery and I find it rewarding to help others.

My partner, son, parents and stepmum deserve a special mention. While the focus suddenly all becomes about you as the patient, it's important not to forget the mental trauma that loved ones also experience. My mum rushed down, as any loving parent would, from her home on the north coast to attend those initial harrowing appointments. My dad and stepmum lived down the road from us in Sydney and were a tremendous support and much needed babysitters. Steve had enough going on with his new job in a new city but managed somehow to stay strong and grounded and keep us all together. It was an enormous task and a huge emotional rollercoaster for all. Words alone cannot express my gratitude.

---

My mottos: The only way out, is through; *and* Whatever it takes

---

## Trust your gut

My advice is that if you are concerned at all about something on your skin, get a skin check by a dermatologist. If in doubt, cut it out. If you want something biopsied, be your own advocate and insist on the biopsy. Trust your gut. If you receive a cancer diagnosis, see a specialist that specifically works with your type of cancer. Seek a second opinion if you're not happy and don't muck around. Connect with fellow patients who have the same cancer – they are good for the soul. Breathe, buckle in, and take one day at a time.

## Eat the cake!

I was on a keto diet prior to my initial diagnosis. I ate no sugar for about eight months and ended up with stage 3 cancer. I became even more extreme with my diet after that and eliminated meat and dairy but still progressed to stage 4. My strict eating habits did nothing that I'm aware of to aid my outcome. Eat normal healthy food and live a normal healthy life. In my opinion, stress is a contributor even though there's nothing scientific to prove it. Slip, slop, slide and seek.

## Be grateful

Finally, be grateful every day and always look for the flowers. Love your family and tell them all the time. We say that life is precious, but it really is, even the small moments. I look at the world very differently now and everything, from beautiful flowers to a bird landing nearby, to sparkles on the water, is completely magnified.

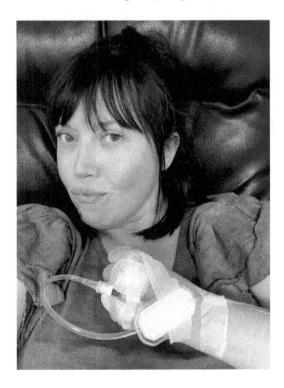

Ruby Stead
*Ruby sadly passed away to melanoma 28th October 2022*

Emma Betts

# Emma Betts

*by her parents Leon and Tamra Betts*

---

It is our wish to continue Emma's legacy – raising awareness about sun safety and the impact of a melanoma diagnosis

---

Our daughter, Emma, was determined, confident, funny, sassy and the youngest of our three daughters. She loved family life and was always the one to organise the family for gatherings. She also liked to voice her opinion and did not have a lot of time for ignorance.

Emma attended the University of Queensland in Brisbane, studying a Bachelor of Arts majoring in peace and conflict studies and international relations. During this time, she became involved in Oaktree, Australia's largest youth-run organisation with over 220,000 members whose focus was to end poverty. She was appointed as the director for Queensland, a real honour, as she was Oaktree's youngest state director at age 18.

Emma followed her passion in life to help those less fortunate and, literally the night after graduation, moved to East Timor to work as a disability support worker. Being surrounded by clinical staff made her realise that she wanted to study occupational therapy and she was accepted into a post graduate degree which was due to start when she returned home. Melanoma, however, was to change the direction of her life.

## The mole

East Timor was not an easy place to live for a 21-year-old young woman, but Emma gained confidence in herself, quickly adapted to the expatriate lifestyle, was having fun and enjoying the challenge.

Whilst scuba diving, a dive instructor noticed a mole on Emma's shoulder as she was removing her wet suit. She was due to come home to Brisbane for a visit a few weeks later and made an appointment with her general practitioner (GP) to have the mole removed. It was sent to a Brisbane pathology group and then forwarded to Sydney for clarification.

## Diagnosis

Emma was initially diagnosed with a 0.6mm stage 1 melanoma. Following re-excision by a dermatologist which gave clear margins, we felt confident that with regular skin checks everything would be OK. At that time, we had heard of melanoma but were unaware of how dangerous it could be if left untreated. We were told that there was only a five percent chance that it could have progressed to Emma's lymph nodes, which was highly encouraging. Emma went back to East Timor and was told to continue being sun smart and to return every three months for review.

In 2013, almost a year later, Emma found a lump under her arm. Her dermatologist had prepared her well for what to look out for, so she packed up early and returned to Brisbane. Within a week, a biopsy was taken which confirmed that the melanoma had spread to her lymphatic system. She was now classified as stage 3 and surgery was booked to remove the lymph nodes from under her arm.

We were told that the odds of survival were against us.

As a family, we were devastated, numb, confused and very scared of how we were going to deal with the progression of the cancer and the deterioration of our daughter. Emma was quite remarkable during this whole journey. She would receive bad news, cry, have many ups and downs but she never complained or asked, 'Why me?' Emma was going to live this life, however long, and give it her best shot.

## Treatment

As Emma carried the BRAF gene, her initial targeted therapy was a combination of dabrafenib and trametinib. Emma was only on this treatment for approximately three months as scans showed progressive disease which indicated that it clearly was not working.

Emma had also met and fallen in love with Serge. Despite telling him to jump ship, he was in it for the long run, and on March 16,

Emma and Serge

2014, they married in what she called an 'amazing wedding.' The wedding was moved forward a few months as she was quite unwell and not responding to initial treatment. Unfortunately, Emma was never able to have children, but Serge and Emma introduced a fur baby into their lives, a cavoodle named Ralph.

Emma was then fortunate to be accepted into a clinical trial for pembrolizumab. She responded very well, but not totally, to this treatment for approximately two years and maintained good general health during this time. She was able to exercise, travel and pretty much enjoyed life regardless. She did however require sinus surgery (which we now believe was a side effect of the medication) and developed vitiligo. This also affected her hair, eyebrows, and eye lashes – her auburn hair turned white/grey. These side effects were, however, a small price to pay.

After two years, Emma was found to have a tumour on her adrenal gland and in a lymph node around her pancreas. These did not respond to pembrolizumab and were growing. She was then put on the combination of ipilimumab and nivolumab. These drugs halted the progression and Emma experienced few side effects but was on pain medication because of the adrenal and pancreatic tumours.

In October 2016, Emma was started on a new drug regime as part of an early clinical trial. Being on a clinical trial gave Emma and our family hope that this drug might be 'the one.' It also provided comfort, as the doctors were watching and reporting back data from ongoing tests.

Scans were always a very anxious time. The week prior to the scan date and then the wait for the results produced what is commonly known as 'scanxiety.' It was always such a relief to hear that there was shrinkage or stabilisation, and this would provide hope that Emma's life may be extended. But when the results were not good, it was heartbreaking. Emma would 'lay low' for a few days to get her head around the news and then move forward.

It was at this point that Emma's condition started to deteriorate. She needed blood transfusions because of low haemoglobin and her pain was managed by visiting nurses. Serge and family members were also trained to administer pain injections. Scans showed that this new drug was not working so she was removed from the trial. It was then decided to cease treatment.

Emma met Jay Allen, The Melanoma Man, early in her diagnosis. He was her first contact with another melanoma patient. Emma admired Jay's determination and achievements, supporting patients and people who have lost a loved one to melanoma. As her melanoma journey began, she documented very raw accounts of her experience in her inspiring and powerful blog, *Dear Melanoma,* which attracted over 25,000 followers. She became dedicated to educating people about melanoma and sun safe awareness and raised money for clinical trials and melanoma research, partly through her online gift business *Love, Emma*. Both remain online. Meanwhile, Jay was preparing to walk from Brisbane to Sydney with the same mission to raise funds for research and to increase public awareness of this wretched cancer. The morning of Jay's departure to Sydney in 2017 was very emotional. Emma cut the ribbon at the commencement of Jay's walk and they hugged and said their goodbyes as Jay left the stadium.

Emma's battle came to an end in hospital in April 2017. Sadly, she did not see Jay complete the walk.

## Preparing for the inevitable

After Emma's terminal diagnosis, it was especially important to us, as a family, to spend as much time as possible together making memories that would be with us for a lifetime. Emma was a wonderful aunt to her two nephews and three nieces, and they returned the love to their Aunty Em. She didn't want them to forget her and so, in her last few months, Emma worked busily to put together memory boxes for each one.

Each day of her illness was taken in her stride. There were 'high fives' for the good results and tears and determination when times were bad. As her disease progressed, some of Emma's personality traits seemed to change. Life was precious, she was on a mission to live a full life and surround herself with positive people, so struggled to understand negativity and selfishness. Emma was thankful for the three years she had. Life was for sharing with loved ones, for making memories, and for preparing for the day when she would no longer be with us. It is safe to say, Emma was in control of her life and how she would live it.

## Legacy and life after loss

Having lived through what we experienced certainly puts things into perspective. These days, it is exceedingly difficult for us to plan events too far ahead. We live more for the moment and we don't sweat the small stuff. Emma's strength influenced our ability to cope and still does to this day; nonetheless, we look back on those years now and do not quite know how we survived.

---

Losing a child is life changing. There is a hole that will not heal.

---

While life will never return to normal, what we do now is live our life around our grief and to do that we carry Emma with us. We often affectionately remember her bossiness and her quirky, cheeky nature. She had an old soul and would announce her arrival into our house with 'Hi Tamra, Hi Leon,' as opposed to 'Hi Mum and Dad.'

We maintain Emma's legacy through *Dear Melanoma* and *Love,*

13

*Emma*. She asked us to keep these going as best we could before she passed away. All profits from *Love, Emma* are donated in support of the Emma Betts PhD Scholarship. This is a scholarship that provides funding to support a PhD research student. We are also involved in advocating for sun safety by telling Emma's story to organisations through a melanoma speaker's hub, and we are on the committee of an annual Brisbane fundraiser.

On Emma's birthday, the anniversary of her death, Mother's Day, Father's Day, and Christmas, we donate to an organisation that provides memory boxes to parents grieving the loss of a child in Brisbane and on the Gold Coast. We feel and understand this grief and it is our way of acknowledging Emma's passing in a positive manner. Also, on these significant days, we place a lit candle next to Emma's ashes. Emma loved candles.

For her secondary schooling, Emma attended St Aidan's Anglican Girls' School. In 2014, she was the recipient of a 'Distinguished Young Alumni' award. Following her passing, the school renamed this award the 'Emma Betts Young Alumni' award. In April 2018, the ABC program 'Australian Story' featured a story about Emma focusing on how her campaigning for better awareness of the disease among her generation has helped to save others' lives. Emma would have been so proud!

## A few words of advice

### Find the right oncologist

Find an oncologist you connect with – someone you can have total faith and trust in. Emma had a wonderful relationship with her oncologist and wanted to know it all – the good and the bad. Her specialist was able to deliver the news in a compassionate way, and Emma had her email and mobile number for 24/7 access.

### Practice good mental health

Never be afraid to seek help from a good psychologist. Emma had regular sessions with a psychologist. Her mum, Tamra, has been seeing a psychologist for about five years. Prior to Emma's passing, the psychologist was able to help Tamra cope with a child with cancer and deal with extended family dynamics. Since Emma's death, she remains someone to talk to during difficult times and a valuable resource when it comes to coping strategies.

*Live life to the fullest*

Every day is a plus regardless of the battle. Don't take anything for granted.

## More information

Dear Melanoma
dearmelanoma.com

Love, Emma
loveemma.com.au

ABC Australian Story, Dear Emma
abc.net.au/austory/dear-emma/9643708

Tamra, Emma, and Leon

Nicole Gillespie

# Nicole Gillespie

*Nicole's story is followed by her parents' perspectives.*

I was born in Brisbane in March 1982 and grew into a fair skinned, blue eyed little girl with dark hair. Little did this girl, the eldest of three children, know she would be facing a challenge in life many go through, but everyone dreads. This little girl always wanted a career. She wants to be a wife and a mother. She wants to continue being the daughter, grandchild and friend that she has been for the last 30 years. But more importantly, she wants to lead a happy, wealthy and, more importantly, healthy life – and to be able to share it with those she loves. Now, this is something that may not be attainable. At the time of writing, this girl is trying to work to pay the bills and other expenses as well as fight the biggest battle of her life ...

## March 2008

At 26 years of age, I went to the GP to get a mole removed. A mole on my upper abdomen which had been there for as long as I could remember had changed. I did not think it was anything serious as it did not appear to be what I, and many others, thought was a typical melanoma. It was round, had a pink-like bubble on it and a halo (a white ring surrounding the mole).

My GP decided to excise the mole and did so there and then. I left with four sutures and was told that the results should be back within the week and to try not to worry too much as it was more precautionary.

The next day I received a phone call from my GP advising me of the results and requesting I see her that afternoon to discuss the next step. I was at work when I received the call and my heart just sank and the tears began to well in my eyes as she told me it came back as a level three melanoma.

What was worse was the next phone call I had to make to my mum.

17

Within the hour, Mum and I were at the doctor's surgery. Sitting there, trying to remain calm as my GP arranged for an urgent surgical appointment with a plastic surgeon, I kept thinking to myself, 'Why me? I never sunbaked or used a solarium. I always put on sunscreen. No one in my family has had it.' They were repetitive thoughts, but I just could not understand why me. My heart sunk and my life began flashing before my eyes.

I was meant to fly to Sydney the next day for one of my best friends' wedding. I had to cancel my trip as I had to have surgery instead. I went in for a day procedure and came out with an 8–10cm wound. I guess I got off lightly given the entire situation at the time!

The results came back. The pathologist reported that they had successfully removed the cancerous cells and that there was no evidence the melanoma had spread to surrounding tissues. Little did I know at the time that I was just at the beginning of the journey.

As part of my follow up as a melanoma patient, I needed to see a dermatologist every three months for the next five years to monitor my skin on a regular basis and to also check my lymph glands for signs of spreading. I saw my dermatologist the week after surgery and, as I had not been before, I was quite uncertain of what I should expect or what I needed to do.

For the unfortunate situation I found myself in, I could not have asked for anything more. My dermatologist made me feel so at ease as she went over my entire body with a fine-tooth comb (and a magnifier!), looking for anything abnormal on my skin. Sure enough, a few moles needed to be excised, but nothing in comparison to what I had already experienced. Again, I did not find the situation uncomfortable as it had to be done and I knew I was being well looked after. This process is now a regular necessity for me. I turn up for my regular appointments, manage my wounds as instructed, and always follow safe sun practice – something I had always done anyway.

## August 2008

In August 2008, I was doing my regular gland checks (under arms and groin) and I noticed a pea-like shape in my right under arm. I monitored it for two weeks to see if it disappeared or grew. After two weeks, I decided to see my GP to have it looked at. She sent me for an ultrasound and, based on their findings whilst I was still there, they confirmed that they needed to do a fine needle biopsy (FNA) of the growth. The radiologist came in and gave me a local anaesthetic and then began the procedure whilst monitoring the ultrasound machine to ensure he was in the right area and had taken a successful biopsy.

Once the procedure was completed, I was informed that the results should be back within the next day or two and I would need to see one of my doctors for the results.

As my GP was away on the Friday, I saw my dermatologist later in the afternoon. I had gone in by myself as mum had gone away for the weekend and I did not want to wait for the results the following week. Regardless of what it was, I just wanted to know.

As I walked into the waiting room, my hands were sweating and shaking, my heart was pounding, and I had all the thoughts from before running through my head. I had not yet had the chance to get married, have kids or even be the successful human resources career woman I always thought I would be and worked hard for.

My dermatologist called me in, and I could tell by the look on her face that the results were not what we wanted. I had been diagnosed with metastatic melanoma. It had entered my blood stream and it was now in my lymph glands. Given the situation, she was fantastic! She had already organised for me to see a leading plastic surgeon who was part of a melanoma unit. She had used him before for other patients and knew he was good so thought he would be perfect, and he was.

I saw my surgeon on the following Tuesday and had the opportunity to research the condition over the weekend. Although I had done my research, I was still given more information on that day about what to expect.

I was scheduled in for surgery two weeks later and was expected to be under general anaesthetic for close to two hours. I would also need to stay in hospital for at least a week.

During the next two weeks, I tried to keep everything as normal as possible. I turned up to work and tried to keep fit so I would have a quicker recovery, but unfortunately my mind was in overdrive and I kept thinking about the future.

As I did not know what to expect long-term at this stage, I got my affairs in order. I ensured I had everything up to date and that it was all clearly labelled should my family need anything in a hurry. The day before I went into surgery, I gave my mum a run-down of where all my important documents were should she need them. I can't even imagine or begin to think what it would have been like for her hearing all of this from her eldest daughter.

The day of surgery arrived, September 11, 2008, and a day I won't forget. I wandered up to level one where I was checked in. The nurses were lovely and all the nerves I had were subtly subdued by their kind and caring nature. I was told to change into a gown, put my little booties on, a red cap and compression stockings – very attractive! Thankfully, the wait to be wheeled down to surgery was not long, although to me 10 minutes seemed like an hour!

My surgeon met me before I was given the anaesthetic and asked if I had any further questions or concerns before he started. I had nothing else to ask and I just wanted to get it over and done with.

I woke up in recovery in agony. My right arm was throbbing from shoulder to fingertip as I had my right axilla removed (axillary glands in right underarm). This also meant that muscles, tendons, nerves, and other tissues had either been removed or affected due to surgery. Approximately 16 of the 33 glands were successfully removed.

For the next two weeks, I had a drain in my underarm to ensure that the lymphatic fluid drained properly as well as any excess blood or tissue from surgery. I was receiving heparin (blood thinner to stop clotting) injections daily and was also on morphine through a drip. Whilst I was at the hospital for a week, my inability to move freely or to do things for myself was a little easier to manage as nursing staff were available to assist, but as most of the pain had gone, I just wanted to go home to the comfort of my own bed and surroundings. It did mean that I needed mum to assist me during this time to ensure I did not cause any further damage to myself – including bathing, wound management, dressing and transport needs. I could not drive for at least a month, so most of my independence was lost during this time.

After close to four weeks off, I was finally able to head back to work. It was a welcome change, and I enjoyed every minute of it.

Normally, I was a very active person. I played sport five days a week – touch football, netball, and gym sessions, but obviously I had to stop of a while. I needed to allow my body time to heal and the high impact sport I was participating in would have slowed my recovery process. Once I was ready again, I was back out there on the sports grounds! Whilst I was in hospital, I also set myself a new challenge – triathlons – and that is exactly what I did when I recovered. I started training and competing!

## July 2010

Two years passed, and I was just starting to think, 'This is great, I am in the clear.' Well, at least I thought so!

As part of my weekly routine, I would still check all lymph node areas including the area which had already been partially removed. On this day, I found another lump, but was hoping it was an inflamed gland from having a mole recently removed. So, it was off to see the doctor again to arrange an ultrasound and biopsy. Sure enough, it was back – metastatic melanoma.

I began arranging appointments again to see my surgeon and had managed to get an appointment on the Tuesday afternoon. As it had recurred in a similar location, I needed to have a CT scan to ensure it had not spread to any other parts of my body.

The waiting game began again.

I went in for day surgery the following day to have the lymph node removed and had the remainder of the week off work. On Friday, I received a call from my surgeon saying that there was evidence on the CT scan of cancer on my pancreas and spleen as well as in my right breast. To confirm this diagnosis, I had to have a PET scan to highlight additional areas and provide a clearer image. Unfortunately, I could not get in to have the scan until the following Wednesday.

Surgery went well and all the cancerous tissue was removed from the area of concern. The surgery was not as invasive, and my recovery was a much quicker process than the time before. I was back at work the following week and was attending medical appointments as needed.

Little did I know that the following Wednesday would be a day from hell. My sister had arranged to take me to hospital to have the PET scan and we were then going to treat ourselves to a sister's day out – shop, lunch and just hang out.

These plans soon changed.

After sitting at the hospital, being injected with radioactive dye, and lying down for the tests for two hours, my mum and stepfather met us at the hospital. Initially I thought, 'Isn't this nice, they want to join my sister and I,' but then I realised it was something more.

The day I had the test was the same day my nana passed away in the morning from a major stroke. My mum and stepfather had met us at the hospital to tell us. Nana had always feared cancer and never wanted to experience it. She had seen me grow up, celebrate milestones and was full of life, and now she had suddenly disappeared. I had visited on the Saturday prior which was the last goodbye. Perhaps she knew. I remember her saying as I walked out, 'Thanks for coming Nicole, make sure you drop in any time.' I am glad she passed away without us telling her what was wrong with me. That alone would have killed her.

I received the official results that Friday. Stage 4 metastatic melanoma. I had multiple tumours throughout my body and surgery was not the best option at this stage. The tears were building, the heart was thumping, but I also had to show mum that I was strong and could beat this. Thankfully it was still at an early stage, but I was still going to have one of the biggest fights of my life ahead of me. I had to tell the other members of my family, including my Pop, who had just lost his wife of 60 years. He had also cared for her full time for the last 30 years as she had suffered a stroke before I was born.

The following week I was at the oncologists. Between the Friday and the Thursday, I researched extensively. I needed to make sure that I had all the information at hand so I could make an informed decision.

I had been told about BRAF – a gene that can cause normal cells to mutate causing cancerous cells. There was evidence that this gene was in some melanoma patients. There was a trial underway and those who had the gene may be eligible to participate. I researched what I could, but I received additional information on the day of my consultation.

Once the decision had been made about what I wanted to do, there were more tests, more scans, bloods, and a whole lot more. The process was long winded, but I did not want to mess around. I wanted this disease out of my body. In brief, I wanted the trial which involved:

- Testing for the gene. Tissue samples had to be sent away to see if I had the gene.
- If BRAF positive (gene causing mutation) – proceed with additional tests including blood tests, CT scans, dermatology checks.
- If there was nothing visible (cancerous cells) on my brain in CT, OK to proceed.
- If not pregnant, OK to proceed.
- If no other skin related cancers, OK to proceed.

## August 2010

After 10 days of waiting to find out if I had the gene, I found out that I was BRAF-positive. There were two arms to this particular trial:

Arm A was going to target the cells which were potentially causing the mutations and cancerous cells to grow, but I did not know of too many of the potential side effects at this stage. The drug would target the BRAF gene.

Arm B was going to be administered as a form of chemotherapy with the unpleasant side effects, but not necessarily target the genes that were involved in melanoma.

The entire testing period went on for about two weeks. After the main results were in, I went in on the Thursday morning to finish off the last few tests. Once the tests were complete, my details were entered into a computerised system. Once entered, the system automatically generated a response advising which arm of the trial I would be participating in. I was selected for arm B and treatment was to start that day. The script was written up. I was shown where I needed to go and my mum, boyfriend and I went and got some lunch and fresh air before it all began.

I went back to the oncology day clinic an hour later. I climbed into the big recliner type chair and had to give more blood samples before being given some anti-nausea medication. The dacarbazine (chemo) was then attached to my IV line and turned on. I knew this was it. The fight of my life had started, and I needed to stay fit, healthy, and focussed to ensure it worked. I have dreams and goals in life, but as mentioned earlier, these needed to be put on hold until I could be 100% healthy again.

The staff at the day clinic were lovely. Although it was an experience that no-one wants to have, they explained everything very well. They made me feel calm, and I was able to ask questions and be relatively comfortable whilst the chemical was pumped into my body for the next hour or so. The staff in this oncology unit need to be commended for what they do. The long, emotional hours would take a toll on them and their families, but they still go in each day to look after others.

I had to endure this process every 21 days, but I couldn't really complain as the end justified the means. Although in saying that, I suffered nausea, lethargy, severe headaches, dry itchy skin, and sensitivity to sunlight to the point where my skin burned. Within the first hour after treatment, it felt like someone was pouring chemicals all over me – my lips, fingers, face, arms and head felt like they were burning, and I could not stop it.

## September 2010

I underwent more treatments in September with the same side effects. After my second treatment, I noticed that my long, thick hair had begun to thin. When I washed it, I would see strand after strand go down the bath. When I ran my fingers through my hair, more thick strands of dark hair would fall out. Thankfully, it was not large clumps of hair, just enough to thin it!

I still tried to work full time, but unfortunately this was not very successful. Each week, I took time off work to attend appointments or to rest because I was too unwell. I was being paid and taking annual leave where possible but knew that the time would come when I had no annual leave left and yet still so many bills to pay.

As I had had two treatments, it was time to check on my progress by having another CT scan. Off I went, fasted and ready to drink the very delightful contrast! I waited patiently for my turn. Regardless of how many times I have done it before, laying on that bed, your thoughts start running wild again and the nerves attack.

The results were ready when I went in for the next treatment. They were not the results I was wanting, but I guess it was OK considering. The tumours were not shrinking. They were growing ever so slightly. I just wanted them to shrink. So, my condition was considered stable at this stage, but the oncologist did indicate that after another two treatments, I would have another scan and if the result was still the same that we would need to consider alternative options including the possibility of travelling interstate for treatment to get the desired results.

I began to tell my body to behave! I was hoping that my body just needed a little more time for it to process the chemotherapy so that it could start working the way we were all hoping for.

## October 2010

October was like the other months. I turned up every three weeks for the same hit of chemo! I started acupuncture to give my body an extra helping hand to process the chemicals with the hope that the tumours throughout my body would indeed shrink. To assist the process, I also officially reduced my hours at work. I did not want to appear unreliable by constantly calling in sick, but I still needed to look after my health and maintain a decent income to pay the normal costs of living.

## November 2010

I had put on a significant amount of weight from the dexamethasone (anti-nausea medication). I was not exercising, except for light walking, and as the dexamethasone was a steroid it increased my appetite. I tried to cut back on the anti-nausea medication to assist me to maintain a healthy weight range, but unfortunately it didn't work. So, after seeing a dietician, monitoring my own diet and increasing my walking regime, I hoped to see some weight reduction.

This month, I also needed to have another CT scan to determine if the tumours were shrinking. The Friday after the scan, I was back in hospital for my treatment and to find out the scan results.

I went through the normal process relating to the trial which included measuring my blood pressure, weight, height and temperature, and completing a questionnaire about my general wellbeing and treatment progress. My mum came with me on this day as it was going to determine my treatment moving forward. Mum's eyes were welling with tears before we even got in there and I could not sit still.

The oncologist called me in. There was some small talk and then we got onto the main topic. The next few words were all I heard initially, 'The tumours have not grown.' I could not change my focus from here for a minute. There was still more to come, 'They have not shrunk either.' After four rounds of chemo, I could not stop thinking about why they had not shrunk. I was doing everything possible to try and maximise the treatment so that the tumours would shrink. No such luck! Although they were not shrinking, it was still positive that the chemo was stabilising the rapidly growing cancer. The best news was yet to come. I had so many questions about where my treatment was now headed and then my oncologist said, 'In the new year, Roche will be giving us the BRAF drug for those who are currently on arm B whose condition is progressing.' Wow! I could not believe it. They were having fantastic results with the BRAF drug, but unfortunately for me, the dacarbazine was only stabilising my condition. Swo, this was an early Christmas present!

This bit of news gave me hope again. I was able to re-focus on the battle of my life.

## January 2011

Christmas came and went along with the New Year celebrations.

My first visit to the oncology department was going to be interesting. Still unsure if the BRAF drug had been approved for the cross over phase, I was unaware what my treatment would involve.

I had my routine bloods, weight, blood pressure and temperature checked and filled out the quality-of-life survey. After that was complete, it was back to the waiting room until it was my turn to see the oncologist.

My name was called and in I went. As I am now a regular around the oncology unit and friendly with my oncology team, I did not beat around the bush – let's just cut to the chase and so I asked if I could go ahead with BRAF. There was no such luck! It was still with the board of ethics waiting on final approval before I could be issued with it. So, it was back to the day ward for chemotherapy again.

The next three weeks went quite slowly, but on the Wednesday prior to my regular appointment I was informed that the BRAF drug had been approved! So, on my Friday visit, I would be able to commence the tablet form of the drug. I was so excited. This was proving to be working for people, so I thought this could be my last chance to make the little buggers shrink!

I started on four tablets in the morning and four at night, daily. I was thinking at the time, 'Gees, tablet form is going to be a breeze.' Well, wasn't I mistaken! Come Sunday, I could not move. I was in agony and could not get any relief. My joints had seized up and I noticed that I started to get a lot of welts on my body. These looked a bit like mozzie bites but were a lot bigger and a large area around the welt was red, inflamed and extremely painful.

I continued taking the tablets but had a follow up appointment at the hospital on the Friday. I was not well at all. I had temperatures, vomiting, diarrhoea, very stiff joints and was extremely sensitive to light. Even if the sun was not out, the UV was enough to cause my skin to burn and become painful. I could not even brush my teeth or butter a piece of bread from the pain in my joints.

Hoping these side effects were only temporary, I battled on and tried to persevere. That weekend, I ended up in hospital. It appears to have been a coincidence that I also ended up with some form of infection, and so I spent the next three days hooked up to a drip and in a share room on the oncology ward. I was very pleased to get home to my own bed on the Sunday!

The following Friday, I went in for another follow up and, given that I was still experiencing such discomfort and pain, a decision was made to stop my new medication for a week to give my body a break and then to recommence on only three tablets in the morning and three at night. The next week, I felt great! No painful joints, no welts –

nothing! It was amazing to realise just how much the drugs were affecting my body physically.

The following weekend I commenced the reduced dose and I felt OK. A few twinges in my joints, but nothing as severe as last time. I was hoping this would be the case for the duration, but the following week the side effects began to creep in again. They were back! All of them! On the bright side, they were a little milder than first time round. This time, I tried various things to see which gave the best relief. Besides morphine-based pain killers, ice packs were OK some of the time and at other times heat packs were better – I just had to trial which one worked best that day.

As the welts were continuing, I had to see the dermatology unit. After reviewing my skin and obtaining another doctors opinion, they felt that not only had I managed to get arthritis with this new drug, but also urticarial vasculitis. This disease is sometimes only evident in hepatitis B or C patients and in those with leprosy, but rarely certain drugs can cause it as well.

It was a relief to know that the drug had caused this particular side effect, but unfortunately there was no way of knowing at this stage how long I would need to be on the drug for. So rather than trying to work out how to stop it, we had to come up with a plan on how to alleviate some of the symptoms.

As I was on a trial drug and everyone responds differently to medications, they ran a large number of tests to confirm the diagnosis as a way to help identify potential problems. This included a puncture biopsy of one of the welts which also meant a couple of stitches.

Some days I would wake up feeling like a crippled old woman – my joints had seized up, my skin was sore, and I could hardly walk, let alone use stairs, sit or lay down. It was so hard for me as I was so active before. I was doing triathlon training, playing touch, and just walking in the evenings, but now everything had stopped and not because I wanted it to but because I had to. These activities provided an outlet for everything, but I didn't have them anymore so had to find something else to do to keep my mind occupied and focussed all the time.

# February 2011 - December 2011

Once I learnt how to manage the side effects of the drug targeting the BRAF gene, I continued to work part time to maintain some normality in life. This also gave me a purpose to get up in the morning. Even though I was working, I was still unable to do the things in life that I had always done due to the side effects.

Over the next few months, the results were promising. Every 8–12 weeks when I had a CT scan, I received the news every cancer patient wants to hear. The nights before receiving the results were sleepless due to anxiety but the words, 'They are shrinking!' made up for it. Some were shrinking faster than others, but in my opinion any shrinkage was good!

These types of results continued throughout the year. Of the five tumours in my body, some were almost gone. On CT scans, they appeared similar to scar tissue, so I was stoked. The tumour on my pancreas was always a tough one though. Although it was shrinking, it was not shrinking as quickly as the others, nor was it shrinking as much as the others. The results were still positive, but this was something that always sat in the back of my mind as a possible issue in the future.

When I began this new drug, I was told by the oncologists that in the majority of patients the drug would only be successful for approximately six to nine months before it stopped working and tumours would begin to grow again. The BRAF gene that the drug was targeting would eventually figure out a way to get around things, allowing the cells to grow again. So as the nine-month mark approached, every appointment became even more nerve racking.

In the middle of December, I had my final CT scan for 2011. I went in for the results, and although I had been on the drug for close to 12 months, I was very wary of the fact that I may be told something I did not want to hear. On this day, I was told that the tumour on my pancreas had grown slightly, but that I was still able to remain on the drug until further reviews of my scans. Despite this, I left the hospital that day thinking it was an early Christmas present. Although there was some growth, only one of the five had grown and I was able to continue the drug that had worked for as long as it had.

My family and I were able to have a wonderful Christmas together! We managed to share it with our extended family, and we had plenty of laughs, ate lots, shared and created lots of memories.

With each scan, I would set goals for how long I hoped the drug would continue to work. After the results I had received, I set a new goal. I wanted this drug to continue working until my 30th birthday on the 2nd of March.

One of my best friends was getting married on New Year's Eve in Sydney, so shortly after Christmas I packed my bags and headed south for what I was hoping would be a fabulous break. I would see lots of friends who I had not seen in a long time, finally meet my friend's baby and have a great time. Little did I know, I would be hit with what felt like a sledgehammer. My oncologist phoned as I literally got off the plane in Sydney and informed me that she had been reviewing my latest scan, had done some further investigation, and found that the tumour on my pancreas had significantly grown, and had in fact almost doubled. The drug was no longer being as successful as we needed it to be. I held it together on the phone, asked if I was to continue the current medication until I was next seen and if I had to do anything else. She informed me to keep everything the same, including the dose, and that we would discuss things upon my return and work out a plan from there.

Although I was expecting this time to come at some stage and thought I had prepared for it, I was a mess! All the original thoughts I had back in the beginning surfaced again. My life was flashing before my eyes – all the what ifs, hows and whys with no answers. My family was back in Brisbane, so I could only speak to them on the phone, but I was lucky to be surrounded by my wonderful girlfriends and their families. I tried to enjoy myself as much as possible and I was glad I was able to spend such valuable time with these wonderful people with whom I had been friends since I was 12, if not 10!

By the time I got back to Brisbane, I was prepared for another battle. Each time I would be knocked down, it would take me a few days to get my head around everything, but I kept telling myself that I could do it. I had to keep fighting and I just needed to get on with it. I needed to show my loved ones that I was strong, not giving up and giving it everything I had (perhaps that was my competitive nature coming out). Even though I was in a situation beyond my control, I needed to stay focussed and get back on the horse, hoping that tomorrow someone will find a cure.

Once I saw the doctor again, there was a bit more direction as to what would happen. I needed to have several more tests before a treatment option would be decided. If there was only the one tumour visible (the one on my pancreas), surgeons would be able to remove it; however, it would involve at least a three-month recovery process as removing your pancreas and spleen is a very large operation. If there were other signs of tumour in my body, I would start on a new form of chemo and have radiation to try and shrink the tumour on my pancreas. Part of me knew that I would not be having surgery. Although all the other tumours were not really visible any more on CT, I felt that the PET scan would show otherwise.

My instincts were right – unfortunately. After CT, PET and MRI scans, the results were in. All the tumours I had originally started with were still visible and active. Pancreas / spleen, right breast, left lung, middle of chest, and near a muscle on my back, which in summary meant that my disease was progressing and quickly.

As a result of the news I received that day, I stopped working. As of the end of January, I retired and became a full-time cancer fighter! Although I was not working as such, I planned to use this time to educate others and help in preventing this deadly disease, not to mention keeping as healthy as possible!

As the tumour on my pancreas was now quite large, it started causing a significant amount of pain and nausea. As well as strong pain medication, radiation therapy was booked to try and shrink the tumour and to stop it causing me pain and discomfort. The radiation was to be conducted over five sessions beginning on February 27. I was also to start a new form of IV chemotherapy known as ipilimumab. This would be administered every three weeks for four cycles before treatment was reviewed again.

Before starting my new treatments, and as my 30th was so close, I wanted a holiday and hoped to head to Fiji with my mum. After discussing the above treatment options with various doctors, everyone agreed it was best for me to take my holiday now before it all began. So, it was off to Fiji four days later for a week of pure bliss! Another girlfriend and her mum, who I had known since I was 10, wanted to join us in Fiji – we had an absolute ball, and it was just like old times. I hoped to be able to do it again soon, that's for sure!

After getting back from Fiji, it was all systems go! I commenced radiation as well as ipilimumab. It was an IV drug, and I was warned about the side effects. The radiation made me feel quite nauseous as it was near the stomach region, but thankfully there were not too many side effects from the drug. I was also lucky that the drug was still in a trial phase and was being funded. Had I started a couple of weeks later, it would have cost $120,000 per 70kg of body weight!!

After having the four cycles of treatment, it was time for another scan. Unfortunately, the results were not what I was looking for. The tumours were growing. At this stage, I did not have too many options left. So, the decision was made to wait a while and see what my body did and then act as needed.

By October 2012, I was starting to experience a lot of nausea and pain. After another scan, it turned out that the disease was progressing quite rapidly and had now also spread to my ovary and there were many new subcutaneous lesions.

The new journey began.

At the age of 28, I began writing my Will for all the wrong reasons. Stage 4 metastatic melanoma has no cure at this stage. Current therapies do work in some cases, but it is not definite. Everyone is different, and given how quickly it grows, I have learnt to live each day as if it were my last. This is something I live by and although it may sound quite morbid, I have an opportunity to do the things I want to do, work through my bucket list (it is quite lengthy and, in some cases, expensive and you need to know or contact the right people!), spend time with those who mean the world to me and make the most of life in general. I am laid back, don't hold grudges, and I try not to sweat the small things – I just get on with it and do what I want to do and what I need to do to keep going.

My private doctors (GP, dermatologist, and plastic surgeon) and the staff at my treatment hospital have been amazing. For the situation I have found myself in, I could not have asked for better care. People quite often ask, 'Why don't you go to a private oncology clinic?' and I always respond, 'I am in the best care, have some of the best doctors in Queensland looking after me, have access to the latest medical equipment and they have a melanoma clinic specialising in the treatment of melanoma.' I cannot ask for anything more, and I cannot thank these people enough for all their hard work and dedication.

Part of my way of dealing with everything is that I want to help others. For me, it is a little too late; however, if I can increase awareness, raise much needed funding, and educate the community, perhaps more lives can be saved from this silent killer, starting with children in primary and high school. For me, seeing others achieve their goals can sometimes be enough, but to prevent someone else going through the same things my family and I have been through, I will do whatever it takes. It is not pleasant, and no one should have to go through cancer, regardless of the type of disease.

*Nicole's fight ended at the tender age of 32.*

\*

*A mother's perspective as told by Kerry*

I am always happy to talk about Nicole's illness to help raise awareness as it can happen to anyone at any age. It keeps Nicole's memory alive, and it is also what she wanted.

For Nicole, it was not about getting sunburnt. As she was fair skinned, she always covered up or used sunscreen. Unfortunately, she had a gene that made her more susceptible.

Nicole was a people person! She started out in hospitality but changed her focus to a career in human resources – she loved helping people. She was school captain in Year 12, not for her academic achievements but more because of her ability to make changes to help her peers! She enjoyed a good laugh and could be very loud! She always spoke her mind and could be very opinionated, but family meant a lot to her. She was fiercely protective of her family and friends, would do anything for them and was very loyal. She did not tolerate negative people! Nicole also loved any type of sport but particularly team sports which she either played or watched. She also loved our dog Molly, a maltese shitzu.

When Nicole was first diagnosed, I was shocked, devastated and confused, but most of all, scared! Why Nicole? How was this journey going to play out? Could I possibly lose my daughter to this disease? For Nev, Nicole's stepfather, it brought everything back as he had been diagnosed with a stage 3 melanoma in 1982 and so he knew what it meant.

And yet through everything there was hope. Nicole participated in several trials over her last four years. One involved flying to Sydney every three weeks for treatment as there was nothing available in Queensland at the time. When a new trial became available, when test results came back with no sign of no new tumours, or when tumours had shrunk, or at best remained stable, it was good! Nearly all the trials extended Nicole's life by 9–10 months on average. We tried to stay positive!

A beacon of positivity, despite everything that was happening, was Jay Allen. Jay contacted Nicole after she was diagnosed with stage 4 disease. He is an amazing human being and I do not know how he does what he does! They hit it off immediately! Nicole would phone into Jay's support meetings. They would chat regularly and catch up whenever Nicole was in Sydney. He was such a great support to her. One of Nicole's last bucket list items was to attend the Logies and Jay helped make that happen! Nicole asked Jay to go with her and had him running around all night as her photographer!

In 2014, Nicole spoke at the first fundraiser in Brisbane. She passed away three months later. We remember Nicole by continuing to participate in fundraisers with a team in Nicole's memory. I have hosted the Brisbane fundraiser since 2015 and will continue to help raise awareness and vital funds for research to find that elusive cure.

Nicole had a wicked sense of humour, but no doubt would like to be remembered for her fighting spirit and her fierce loyalty to her family and friends. She never got to meet her niece and five nephews but there are days when I look at some of them and see a bit of Nicole's personality, and that makes me smile. She would have been the best aunty!

There are no real words to describe what it is like to lose a child. I can just simply say that we should not forget how important life is. Surround yourself with people you want to be with and try not to sweat the small stuff. The experience puts things into perspective.

---

Nicole's favourite sayings: 'Do something amazing every day'; and 'You only live once, but if you do it right, once is enough' – Mae West

---

## Looking back

I had no idea Nicole had been documenting her journey until she passed away. Even though it has been nearly seven years, and despite it always being in the back of my mind, I still had not read it. It wasn't until I had contact with Aileen regarding documenting Nicole's story for Jay's book that I knew the time had come. It then took me a couple of months to actually sit down and read it. There never seemed to be the right moment. I realise now I lived those four years after Nicole was diagnosed as stage 4 in a total blur. I was on auto pilot just doing whatever I could for her or what I thought I needed to do. I sat in on all the appointments and waited on test results.

We travelled together, we laughed together, and we butted heads – a lot (she could be so hard on me at times), but we hardly ever cried together.

Looking back, I feel that she was trying to make me a stronger person so that I would be able to cope better when she was gone. We were both trying to be strong for each other and I still struggle with that now. This piece by Gwen Flowers sums it up perfectly for me:

# Grief

### by Gwen Flowers

I had my own notion of grief.
I thought it was the sad time
That followed the death of someone you love.
And you had to push through it
To get to the other side.
But I'm learning there is no other side.
There is no pushing through.
But rather,
There is absorption.
Adjustment.
Acceptance.
And grief is not something you complete,
But rather, you endure.
Grief is not a task to finish
And move on,
But an element of yourself
An alteration of your being.
A new way of seeing.
A new definition of self.


*A father's perspective as told by John*


I am so proud of how Nicole handled the whole process from diagnosis and treatment to recurrence and more treatment. It was an emotional battle as much as a physical one. She wanted to beat the disease and go on to lead a normal life. We received good and bad news along the way but eventually it came down to a losing battle but one she had fought hard.

When Nicole passed it was gut wrenching. Even though we knew it was coming it was a great loss. I felt like I was in a vacuum as you really cannot prepare for it. As a parent, you do not expect to see your child pass before you do. You want to protect your child and you feel guilty that you are unable to stop it. More than seven years have now passed, and you reflect on the many things that Nicole has not been here to celebrate amongst family and friends. She now has six nephews and nieces that she cannot enjoy nor are they able to benefit from the positive influence she would have brought to their lives.

When Nicole was first diagnosed with melanoma, we were optimistic and positive that she would get treatment, that everything would be good, and that life would return to normal. Nicole received good results after the first round of treatments, and everything seemed to be heading in the right direction. She had lymph nodes removed, which created some future issues such as not being able to take blood pressure readings or have intravenous lines inserted on that arm, but it was a relatively small price to pay for survival. Nicole was still living in Sydney at that time and continued to work and study, but subsequently moved back to Brisbane where her mum Kerry, and brother and sister Ben and Laura, were also living. She was a very confident, strong willed and positive person and had a 'I'll beat this' attitude – a great attribute when you are dealing with something with so many unknowns.

When Nicole received her second diagnosis, she continued to do everything to fight the disease and met up with other sufferers in Sydney to share her story. She spoke at a smaller group at Brisbane's Bayside and shared her diagnosis and treatment with the group with great feedback. Fundraisers in Brisbane soon developed, firstly at West End, then at Riverstage in the city's botanical gardens. Nicole's mum Kerry, stepdad Neville, and family and friends pulled together to organize the event to raise funds and awareness about melanoma and it has grown each year. There were speakers, entertainment, raffles, food trucks and a walk through the area. Unfortunately, now with Covid-19 in our midst, these events have had to be postponed, at least physically.

Nicole was determined to beat this horrible disease and was ready to jump on any new treatment that came along as existing treatments failed to control her melanoma. She wanted to be a part of clinical trials on promising new treatments, but some of these were only available to people with specific chromosomes/genes that the new drugs targeted. She felt like a winner when she was tested and found to have the BRAF gene and was therefore eligible to participate in a trial, run by an American pharmaceutical company, which was only available to patients who were running out of options with normal treatments. These drugs would have come at an enormous cost had they not been covered by the pharma company as part of a trial. The new treatments aimed to harness the body's immune system to help fight the disease, and while there have been some excellent results, they unfortunately do not work for everybody.

---

At this stage, we were waiting and hoping for a miracle discovery and cure, but it never came ...

---

Nicole received treatment with good results almost immediately – there were no new tumors, and the existing ones were reducing in size, which was very positive. She had to have ongoing tests and, after about nine months, some tumors started to reappear which meant an immediate stop to the experimental drugs and back to traditional treatments (chemotherapy and radiation) as new tumors ravaged new areas of her body. The treatments were at times very harsh: skin burns from radiation, side effects from chemotherapy, some hair loss, weight gain and the need to take strong pain killers. This was horrendous for a young woman to be going through and yet she did not complain as she was determined to beat it. With each treatment and testing, Nicole's oncologist told her there were no new treatments and that her condition had become terminal. Any treatment at this stage aimed to keep her as comfortable as possible. This was harsh news, but Nicole wanted it up straight with no softening of the message. I remember being at work on a day of one of Nicole's important test results. The results showed that she was terminal, and no new treatments were available. I spoke to her on the phone. It was a real shock and so hard to handle. I had to leave work immediately, completely devastated by the news. Nicole's blood counts were down, and she also needed blood transfusions to get the counts back up.

## 2014 – the bucket list

The year 2014 was very full on. Nicole's health was deteriorating, and there was no time guarantee. Laura was engaged to Kerri and they were planning to get married later in the year with Nicole to be Laura's maid of honor. Nicole was very excited about the marriage, wanted to get involved and carry out the role in its entirety. With the uncertainty of time, Laura and Kerri decided to bring the wedding forward to April to ensure that Nicole would be there. There were some challenges, but the wedding went off beautifully. Nicole's health had deteriorated by then and she had to sit down all night. I thank Laura and Kerri tremendously for changing the date to ensure Nicole was a big part of their day.

Nicole had a bucket list of things she wanted to do. She was very determined, straight to the point and sometimes a bit too outspoken, but this helped her to push ahead and tick off as many items as possible. Healthwise she might have been better off resting, but Nicole was so determined that she went ahead with as much as she could. These included a trip to New York and London, travelling up front on an A380 aircraft, flying over Uluru, and a Fijian holiday with her mum and her best friend from school days.

Nicole loved Queensland and her beloved Broncos rugby league team as well as the Queensland State of Origin team. She had breakfast with the Broncos and attended a Queensland State of Origin dinner. She was able to sit in the player area at ANZ Stadium in Sydney with the Queensland Origin team and was invited on field when the team and coach Mal Meninga received the winning trophy during Queensland's 8-year winning dynasty.

Nicole also loved Australian produced TV shows and soapies, with *Home and Away* a favourite. She was invited to visit the set in Palm Beach in Sydney and meet some of her favourite actors. She also received an invitation to attend the 2014 TV Week Logie Awards at Crown in Melbourne and was dressed by one of Australia's leading designers. Not being shy, Nicole did not wait for introductions. She bowled straight up to the people she wanted to meet and introduced herself. It was a very late night which was tiring for her, but it did not hold her back. Just five short weeks later Nicole passed.

## Support along the way

Nicole and Jay

Nicole was supported in her journey by Jay Allen who helped to turn some of Nicole's bucket list into reality. Jay makes genuine friends with so many people and gives his time and support, but with this comes the reality of losing close friends to this disease.

Since Nicole's passing, I have had a lot more to do with Jay. I want to support him in his journey to raise awareness and funds and consider him a close friend. Through various activities relating to melanoma awareness, I have forged new friendships and met wonderful people, although the common bond we share is truly a tragic one.

Jay did an initial walk from Sydney to Melbourne in 2014 – it was a major effort! Kerry was invited by Jay to cut the starting ribbon. Naturally, Jay's determination saw him go one bigger and in 2017 he walked 1000 kilometres from Brisbane to Sydney starting at Suncorp Stadium and finishing at Barangaroo in the CBD 30 days later. I volunteered to do a section from Pottsville in New South Wales (NSW) where I was living to Byron Bay, a mere 43 kilometres. It was a big day and very rewarding. Jay needed a massage each day after the walk, ice baths and treatment for blisters, but he powered on including through some horrific weather. I travelled with my good friend Mark Humphries to Sydney to complete the last section of the walk from Brookvale Oval in Sydney's northern beaches to Barangaroo via the Sydney Harbour Bridge. It was a very emotional finish and wonderful to be a part of it.

Jay wanted to go even bigger and organised the next walk from Adelaide to Sydney, a full 2000 kilometres in 50 days with Jay walking every leg together with support walkers and a support crew. I put my hand up to be part of the support crew. It was very important to ensure the safety of walkers and we made sure they had adequate water, snacks, and meals available during the day. It was another great event with wonderful people and mixed weather from cold mornings to warm days and dust storms. I started in Adelaide for the first week and made it to Bordertown, then returned home and rejoined the crew in Kiama NSW for the last week up to Sydney. We were met at Government House with a warm welcome from the NSW Governor. The memories will last forever. I think and hope that Nicole would have been proud that I supported Jay and the cause, and I will continue to do so in her honour.

---

Thank you, Jay, for what you do, and for the support and friendship you gave Nicole in her melanoma journey. All the best to you and your beautiful family.

---

# Final reflections

Melanoma commonly affects younger people in the 18 – 39 age group. Many cancers affect people in much older age groups, and while a cancer diagnosis is devastating and difficult to deal with at any age, it is particularly hard on younger people. Many of the people Nicole met were also in this age group. Some treated their diagnosis and prognosis differently; some chose to stop treatment and to pass at home with loved ones. This is a very personal decision and I respect people to be able to make their own call. Nicole chose to fight to the end and take whatever treatment was available, all the time hoping for a miracle cure. As a result, I am sure she was afforded extra time and she made the most of it to do as many things on her bucket list as possible. I am so proud of her positive attitude along the way. I would have traded places with her if it had been at all possible …

Katie-Lee

# Katie-Lee Spence

*by Debi Spence*

---

'I don't just want to be a photo on a bedside table.'
As difficult as it was for Katie to put herself out there and tell her story, she wanted to try and save people from going through what she did. I feel I should honour her wishes and continue her legacy.

---

Katie was my second child and only girl. She has an older brother who she adored, and he and his wife were incredibly supportive of her when she was diagnosed with melanoma – first at age 18, followed by metastatic disease when she was just 29 years young.

We have a very strong family unit and family was everything to Katie. She loved to run and exercise and would often run five kilometres from her house in Townsville, Queensland, to her grandmother's. We are also very much a dog loving family and Katie was always surrounded by her pets – bulldog Harry, maltese Billy Boy, and a red cattle dog named Dougie. She was a beautiful, intelligent young woman who was incredibly brave and strong.

Katie had a kind heart but was also very tough and practical when it came to dealing with anything. She could be a little bit naughty and loved to party and have a good time, and she had a large and loving friend base. Katie also loved to travel. She travelled overseas several times and even lived and worked in the UK. She eventually met her wonderful husband, Duncan MacLeod, and they had a beautiful daughter Violet. They had planned on having another child and then hopefully adopting from overseas, preferably from Africa given Duncan's heritage.

Katie decided she wanted to be a nurse when she was about 15 and worked hard to achieve her goal. She ended up being a cardiac nurse and eventually worked in private practice with a group of cardiologists. Her patients loved her and were devastated when they learned of her diagnosis and subsequent passing. I was only talking to someone from the practice the other day who told me that a patient had said to her just last week, 'It is not the same without Katie-Lee.' She was much loved by the medical community in Townsville, and they rallied around her from the minute she was diagnosed. As one of her nursing friends said, 'Her beauty captured your attention. Her personality captured your heart.' This summed Katie up so perfectly that we engraved these words onto her headstone.

---

Katie loved life and lived it to the full, almost like she had a lot to fit into a limited amount of time. Sometimes when people pass they leave barely a ripple behind, but with Katie it was a tsunami!

---

## Diagnosis and treatment

Katie noticed a mole on her upper right arm. She went to a doctor who was supposed to be an expert in the field, but he failed to remove it even though she had the warning signs: fair skin, blonde hair, and light eyes. He gave her some concoction to paint on her arm and it turned the mole really black. Luckily, about 10 weeks later, she went to see our normal GP about another matter. He noticed it and told her it should be removed. The pathology came back as melanoma and Katie had to undergo further surgery. We thought and hoped that things would be fine and that this would be the end of it, and it was, but only for 10 years and 4 months…

---

Katie always said that our GP gave her an extra 10 years of life.

---

Katie was diagnosed with metastatic melanoma when she was 29 and her daughter was just seven months old. She had been suffering with a very sore shoulder which she put down to the way she was sleeping. One morning, she woke up with excruciating abdominal pain and Duncan rushed her to the ED. They discovered a mass in her ovary which turned out to be metastatic melanoma. It had also spread to her bones and various other areas in her body.

That day, we experienced complete and utter devastation and disbelief. The thought that I could lose my beautiful daughter and that Katie's adorable little girl might grow up without her incredible mother was very real.

Katie travelled to Sydney for review and treatment. The people at the centre she attended were fantastic and did everything they could to try and give her more time. The travel was hard, but it was the least of her concerns. She told her treating doctors to be as brutal as they needed to be as she would do whatever it took to beat this thing. She had the BRAF gene, and this filled us with hope at the beginning. It was almost like winning lotto! Unfortunately, we were told that the drug which targeted this gene generally only worked for about seven months, and this is exactly what happened with Katie. She required a rod to be implanted in her leg because one of the tumours had cracked the bone. She also received immunotherapy as well as radiation to her brain. She passed away while still on treatment just three weeks after her 30th birthday.

## Remembering Katie-Lee

I know the things that people remember about Katie-Lee, and all the things that I remember about her, like her witty sense of humour, but the only thing that would have mattered to Katie would be to be remembered as a good mother. Most of all, she would have liked her daughter to remember her. As Violet was too young to have any memory of her mother, it is up to us, her family, and friends, to share our stories. Not a day goes by where we don't speak about Katie-Lee. We talk about her constantly – when you stop speaking their name they really are gone.

Katie started a charity called Violets and Lace and we have tried to continue her message of awareness and education through the charity. The charity is run by her friends with my involvement. Jay Allen is also a great supporter of Violets and Lace and we consider him family. He is devoted to searching for a cure for melanoma through his fundraising and I cannot put into words what that means to me.

Through Violets and Lace we have been actively fundraising too. On Katie's 30th birthday, we held a ball and Katie stood up on stage and invited everyone back for her 35th. We kept her invitation and held a masquerade ball. For about five years, we hosted A Tea Party To Remember on Mother's Day. We have had Melbourne Cup functions and Fashion for Kate where we sold second-hand clothes. Unfortunately, the fundraising has come to a bit of a halt with COVID. We have donated a lot of what we have raised to a research foundation in honour of Katie-Lee. Her memory lives on …

# Jennifer Thulborn

I was told that my chances of this cancer spreading and becoming terminal were real.

I was 30 years old when I was first diagnosed with melanoma in 1994. I noticed a small black mole on my back between my shoulder blades. A biopsy performed by my GP confirmed the diagnosis.

Jennifer

At the time, I had two young children with my then husband under my wing – Brittney (aged 3) and Elly (12 weeks). Back then, there was no support or awareness available for this disease. Most of my family and friends did not know much about melanoma and believed that once it was cut out that I would be fine. However, I knew different. I felt quite alone and just had to suppress it all and move on with life, which I did. I wanted more children but was initially told that it would be too dangerous as pregnancy could increase the risk of having more melanoma appear. However, two years later an oncologist advised that the statistics had changed and that I should have another child if it was what we wanted. We went on to have two – Monique and then Fraser.

In 2010, having moved on from the father of my children, I married Tony. Happy years should have followed but very soon after came the diagnosis of stage 4 melanoma. It had spread to my brain and lung. It changed our lives significantly in so many ways and the hardest part was seeing the heartache in my children's eyes.

---

I vowed to spread awareness, seek support, and support others during my own journey of survival.

---

I underwent surgery to remove tumours from my brain and then started on the BRAF drug Zelboraf™ (vemurafenib). Other surgeries followed interspaced with stereotactic radiosurgery followed by the immunotherapy drug Opdivo® (nivolumab). I experienced multiple side effects throughout including loss of peripheral vision, reduced cognitive skills, fatigue at times, severe rashes, loss of hair, and pneumonitis in my lungs. It was always day by day until I participated in a clinical trial. I believed the trial would probably be my last roll of the dice and the beginning of the end, but the trial saved my life!

## Life, loss and love again

I now have real hope of long-term survival. I always searched for survivors to give me hope that I, too, could survive despite the odds stacked against me. I found many and became friends with some of them. We all belong to a wonderful club – the survivor's club! Our hope is that everyone diagnosed with melanoma can be a survivor of this disease. One club member and friend is Jay Allen.

Jennifer and Jay

Jay has been a huge part of my melanoma journey and provided me and my family with so much support. Every two weeks, I would fly, nearly always on my own, from the Gold Coast to Sydney for my immunotherapy treatments. Jay would pick me up and drop me back at the airport after my treatment and scans. He was a life saver! We always had a laugh and often a coffee and a donut just before heading to the airport. This gesture made something so daunting so much more bearable. I will never forget what Jay did for me.

You would think that melanoma was enough of a curveball for anyone to deal with in one lifetime, but in April 2020 my husband and I separated. He found happiness but sadly, in January 2021, he passed away from Australia's leading cause of death for males – coronary heart disease. Throughout it all, my toy poodle, Noah, played a major part in keeping me together.

Life does go on and sometimes it throws unexpected surprises. I now have hope that I will remain around to participate in my four adult children's lives. I've already had the gift of sharing milestones with them that didn't seem possible not that long ago. I hope to travel post-Covid19 and experience new places. My dream destination is the UK so I can discover my heritage. I plan to make the rest of my life my best life, and now I have a special someone to share it with too!

With stage 4 melanoma, a large part of the time I was so depressed that I had pretty much given up on life. Being able to see a future, let alone finding myself happy and in love, was just not a part of the picture. Today, I'm loving my life for the first time in years! Craig was my childhood neighbour who came back into my life as my confidant and best friend. I feel now that I have a future and Craig is certainly a part of it!

Jennifer and Craig

I am now extremely blessed to have only a few side effects and I am living a wonderful life.

## Advice

I have learnt through this experience that life is short and to live each day the best you can – don't sweat the small stuff! Set boundaries for yourself and stop being a people pleaser. I also now have a much greater understanding of how others feel and react when diagnosed with a terminal illness.

My advice to anyone who is diagnosed with melanoma is that today's diagnosis is not the end but the beginning of a new chapter in your life. It won't be easy, so take one day at a time and get lots of rest. Reach out to positive people and let go of the negative. Find the right support. And finally, trust your medical team, but do not be afraid to seek second opinions.

Leah | image: Gez Xavier, Mansfield Photography

# Leah Debono (née Martin)

*by her parents Lex and Heather Martin*

---

There is a very important message in Leah's story. It's quite simple – get a regular skin check! Follow your instinct and seek a second opinion if you're not happy, and always ask to see your test results. It may save your life!

---

Leah was born on July 23, 1987. She grew up on the northern end of the Central Coast of New South Wales, along with her sisters Esther and Nadine. She was an aunty to Mason (Esther and Brendan's son) and to Parker who was born after she passed away. She was married to Ben and was just 29 years young when she lost her battle with melanoma.

Leah had a very strong personality. She was a very independent, determined, and caring person. She loved children and animals. As a family we enjoyed many snow, beach and camping holidays. As a young woman, Leah continued to enjoy the same holidays and travelled overseas with friends. She loved to party and socialise with her friends, whether it be shopping, travelling, or going to music festivals or concerts.

Leah started working at Best & Less while still at school. She was undecided on her career path so when Best & Less offered her a full-time traineeship she accepted. She worked with Best & Less for 15 years. It didn't take long before she became a store manager, and she was often sent to set up new stores. She was a trouble shooter, but most of all she liked to help and train people. Leah was a well-liked, hardworking, and respected employee who received many awards in recognition of her dedication to Best & Less.

## Meeting Ben changed Leah's life

Leah had an ugly mole on her right forearm. She sought medical advice about it twice and had it dismissed twice as nothing to worry about. Having just met Ben, she decided she wanted the ugly mole removed for cosmetic reasons. Unfortunately, the pathology results came back as a Clark level 4 malignant nodular melanoma. It was February 2013, and to say that we were shocked as a family is an understatement. There was no history of melanoma in the family.

## System failures

Leah was placed in the care of a melanoma unit and had her melanoma excised. She then underwent a second surgery, an axillary clearance, but otherwise received no further initial treatment. We were all very positive that it was the end of this glitch in her life. She then went on to have check-ups every six months. During this period, we heard of new breakthroughs in melanoma treatment which gave us some hope should it ever be needed. Leah was doing so well and then the medical system failed her again.

In April 2016, Leah's most recent CT-scan report was essentially lost. At her appointment at the melanoma unit in September 2016, Leah was told that all was well. She left feeling very relieved and was able to look forward to her wedding day. However, the doctor at the melanoma unit did not check his records properly and, in fact, referred to a CT scan report that pre-dated her April scan. Unfortunately, we discovered this massive error after Leah had passed away. The 'lost' April CT scan report had been faxed to the melanoma unit but it was either never seen, or not acted upon. The report stated: *Two new small left upper lobe pulmonary nodules are seen, indeterminate for pulmonary metastases. A short term follow up study in 3 months interval may be considered. No other appreciable change is noted since the previous study.*

In November 2016, Leah began suffering from severe headaches. She sought medical advice and again was told that it was nothing to be concerned about and that it was stress related. A few days later, Leah collapsed at work. She had a brain tumour which was removed at a hospital in Sydney. At this point, further scans found cancer in most of her major organs. We can only wonder if things would have been different had that April scan not been lost. Leah may have been able to commence treatment before the cancer had completely metastasised. As a family, we put our trust in the medical profession expecting Leah to receive the best possible care, but it wasn't the case. We therefore instigated a London Protocol investigation through the hospital and the Health Care Complaints Commission (HCCC) but found that the doctor was well-protected. Our aim in investigating the errors was to ensure that better protocols and systems would be implemented to prevent similar situations happening to other patients and their families.

We stayed positive and Leah went on to receive one treatment of Opdivo® (nivolumab) plus Yervoy® (ipilimumab) in the hope that it would give her a chance at survival. However, by Christmas of 2016, all hope was gone. Leah passed away on January 5, 2017.

The medical system failed Leah on many levels. The most crucial being at her initial consultation in 2011. If only the doctor had done a biopsy then, the outcome of her melanoma journey and her life could have been so different. It is difficult to comprehend that one person can have so much bad luck and that so many tragic mistakes were made.

---

Cancer can affect anyone at any age. Never did we think that we would lose one of our children to cancer. Our lives are not the same.

---

## Remembering Leah

Leah is in our thoughts every day. We love and miss her very much. We miss the vibrant young woman she was. We have a memorial chair on the shore of Lake Macquarie where family and friends can visit, sit, and reflect on Leah's memory. It is also a place where we can meet up with her friends to celebrate her life.

Leah was very positive throughout her illness. We were very proud of her strong morals and personality and everything she achieved. She touched many people. They admired, respected, and thanked her for being in their lives both personally and professionally.

We smile when we remember Leah on her wedding day. She was so happy to be marrying Ben. It was such a wonderful day for all her family and friends to share their happiness. We were all so excited for their future together. They had so many plans – a honeymoon travelling around Australia, building a new house, and starting a family.

Leah

On that day we were all unaware that cancer had spread throughout her body. It is hard to believe that Leah was a beautiful bride on October 1, 2016 and gone just a few months later.

# Meeting Jay

When Leah recovered from her surgeries in 2013, she decided to support research efforts by attending one of the fundraising walks every year. As a family, we went along to support Leah and to help raise funds and awareness.

We met Jay Allen during his 2017 walk from Brisbane to Sydney. Leah had told us about Jay and had planned to walk with him on a Central Coast leg. Unfortunately, she passed away just a few months before. Ben and Nadine walked with Jay in honour of Leah. Since then, we have formed a wonderful relationship with Jay. He is one of the most positive people you could hope to meet, and the sacrifices he makes to raise awareness and funds for melanoma research puts most of us to shame. In memory of Leah, we have supported Jay's walks. We've walked with him and helped as part of the support crew, and we intend to support him with future endeavours.

Peter Selig

# Peter Selig

Telling Peter's story makes me feel better, even if I cry.

*by Narelle and John Selig (Peter's parents) and Belinda Selig (Peter's wife)*

## Narelle and John's perspective

Peter grew up in the Sutherland Shire south of Sydney. As a child, he had lighter skin colouring than his father, his sister, or even I. He was also a red head, just like his grandmother. Both risk factors for melanoma. Peter was a funny and happy sort of good guy with lots of mates from school. His life, when younger, centred around music and he played piano. He became an electrician, which he was rightly proud of, and it made him.

Our son was 25 years young when melanoma took hold.

On Boxing Day in 2003, my daughter, who is a vet, had also noticed a black and bleeding mole on Peter's back when he took his shirt off. This marked the moment our nightmare began. Sydney was full swing into holiday mode and so the local GP specialising in skin took a biopsy and sent it off for analysis. A wider excision was done on his back a few days later which complicated any mapping process. And that was it. We knew that melanoma was a killer. It became a watch and wait process. Peter underwent regular ultrasounds on the glands under the armpits and in the groin area and this continued for some years until the bigger bomb hit in 2008.

At that point there was no cure and no real treatment options. We were told that chemotherapy or radiation therapy would not work on this sort of cancer. Peter had part of his bowel removed and the careful doctors said he would need a (colostomy) 'bag'. His first words after the operation were, 'No bag, Mum! No bag,' thank God. Later, he would go on to have a hemi-hepatectomy, which took out about 60 percent of his liver, followed by another admission for a collapsed lung.

In September of 2009, Peter took part in a clinical trial that was being offered at a Sydney hospital. The cancer unit looked like a war zone! The drug(s) appeared to be working with some positive results, but by December 16 of that year, Peter's results were not at all favourable and his treatment on trial was stopped. There was another clinical trial in the works, but it still needed to be approved by the various ethics committees. He was able to be home for Christmas, but he knew it would be his last.

Through all of this, there was one ray of sunshine when Pete's wife, Belinda, told us she was pregnant. She gave birth to baby Koby and moved in with us for that last year. Jay Allen was also part of our journey. We first saw him when he was on RPA, followed by the crusade to put an end to sunbeds. He is a warrior of a man and we hold him dear to us.

Peter, Belinda, and Koby at Koby's christening

*Peter died just short of his 32nd birthday.*

## Reflections

Peter was a happy person, and it was a great shock for him to learn that he had cancer. He was prepared to do anything to get better, and was stoic, often silent, trying to care for his family and always hopeful. When we think of him, we try to remember the funny or comic moments. He would pretend to be a koala by putting a spoon on his nose backwards and showing his baby son.

I feel for my daughter-in-law who lost a good man in Pete. She was cheated out of having a fairy-tale first year with her new-born and was running around various hospitals (seven in total!) for Peter's treatment throughout. She had to carefully manage Koby's feeds, find a place to feed or express milk, and then there were the parking issues to deal with. All this time, her friends were just enjoying their babies at home. She somehow managed to keep it together. The experience has, however, brought us closer together and we are glad for that.

---

Peter said, 'Don't forget me, Mum.' How could I possibly ever forget my one and only son?

---

## Belinda's perspective

---

There are not enough words to honour Pete, but wow, we lost a good one!

---

Pete had big plans if or when he made it through his battle. He wanted to reach so many people who were going through what he was going through and really wanted to make a difference in people's lives. If he had of made it through his cancer journey, he said he would be right beside Jay getting the awareness out there, walking hundreds of kilometres to raise funds for research, and speaking to the community about melanoma. He really wanted to survive and to be able to tell his story and help others. This is why Pete's journey needs to be shared. He did not get the opportunity to do so and I, together with his family, will carry on for him. We hope that a little bit of Peter John Selig can touch someone through his story.

Pete was a qualified electrician, a hard and dedicated worker. Music ran through his veins. He had an eclectic collection of hundreds of CD's, played the piano, taught himself the guitar and drums and he embraced all genres. He loved photography, was good at it, and wanted to do a calendar of gorgeous sunrises and sunsets and call it 'Horizons'. He loved people and whoever he was around loved his presence. He was raised with strong values and morals, reflected in his ability to really listen, value what you had to say and help out in anyway. Anyone who was close to Pete knew that he truly was genuine, caring, and present when he was in your company.

Pete knew how to make you feel comfortable and he also knew how to make you laugh! He was very funny! A day never went by when he wouldn't make me, or whoever was around him, laugh. He'd tell jokes and make funny prank calls to family and friends pretending to be (complete with a Swedish accent), 'Helmut – the massage therapist with ze rubbing and ze oils.' Even at his sickest, he was still cracking jokes saying things like, 'Gee, you look radiant today,' as you walked into his room in your work or daggy clothes.

## The diagnosis

Pete had a mole in the centre of his mid back. It was quite large, and he kept knocking it while at work while he was climbing up into small spaces. I kept telling him to go and get it checked as it kept bleeding. It was 2003 when he finally did. The doctor he saw at the time was not his usual GP. We went to a skin cancer clinic in our local area where the doctor performed a biopsy which came back as melanoma. The doctor then did a wide excision, stitched him up and referred him to a hospital skin cancer unit to see a professor. Pete's initial diagnosis and treatment was not carried out correctly. We were unaware at the time, of course, but the wide excision complicated any mapping of the area for proper staging and diagnosis. The specialists did not know where the melanoma may have stemmed from; for example, the groin or the top part of Pete's body where the lymph nodes were, so they presumed and guessed that because his primary was in the centre of his back that any traces of cancer in the future would go to the top lymph nodes under his arms. He underwent a PET scan and ultrasound every six months initially and then yearly for four years. All were clear during that period.

In 2008, the cancer came back. Not in his top lymph nodes as expected, but in his groin and stomach area. It was a time when things for us as a young married couple should have been happy. We were about 20 weeks pregnant with our first child, having been trying for about a year with two early miscarriages along the way. Pete noticed that he was very tired all the time, very anxious and couldn't figure out why. He could barely stand up as he was so dizzy and very, very pale. For a normally healthy and active young man, this was very abnormal. I sent Pete straight to the doctor for blood tests not thinking that this would be the start of our nightmare.

That afternoon, Pete was admitted to hospital and had a blood transfusion as the doctors were not clear on what was wrong with him. Then he remembered, 'Oh yeah, in 2003 I had a melanoma removed.' More tests were immediately conducted revealing a golf ball sized tumour in his small intestine which was confirmed to be metastatic melanoma. It was shattering to say the least. The enormity of what was ahead really did not hit us until we knew there were no real treatment options. Pete looked at me and asked, 'Am I going to die?' I said, 'No,' but we both knew that was going to happen. It was a question of when.

Peter underwent a very big operation. He had a small bowel resection and was in intensive care followed by a three-month recovery period. Surgery was our only and best option for treatment at the time.

About three months later, when Pete had recovered from his surgery, our son Koby was born. Koby brought so much happiness in a very uncertain time in our lives. Pete was such a proud dad. He loved every moment and did not leave my side throughout the long 22-hour labour. From that moment on, he was up with me for each feed during the night. He just loved being a dad and a husband.

In 2009, just before Koby turned one, we discovered tumours in Pete's liver which meant another major surgery. Sixty percent of his liver was removed, and he spent 11 days in hospital including two in intensive care. After this, Pete did one round of the highest doses of chemotherapy you could do just so he knew that he had tried absolutely everything to fight it. It made him so sick, and it was awful to witness.

A few months later, we found that there were more tumours which were inoperable located in Pete's spleen, chest wall, what was left of his liver, small intestine, and neck lymph nodes. Each day, there were new tumours growing and popping up all over his body. He was able to access one of the first trials for melanoma, the BRAF trial, as the genetic makeup of one of his biopsied tumours had the BRAF gene. The treatment worked to some extent in that he had a global reduction, but three months into treatment it stopped working. Little did we know that Pete's tumours harboured two genes, BRAF and another. A trial was due to open for the second gene, but Pete did not qualify for it as he was just too sick at the time.

---

Pete offered to be cut open and to have his tumours biopsied so he could do something to help the research advance.

---

We had run out of options. Being told those words from the medical professionals who wanted so much to save him were unbearable and they cried with us. After the trial drug stopped working, the tumours grew and grew and that was it. Pete became more and more ill. We endured multiple trips to the emergency department for collapsed lungs and to drain the ascites that had built up around his stomach then and there. Pete remained in hospital in palliative care. He held on for three long and gruelling months, never giving up. His mind was sharp, but his body was riddled with cancer and complications. He had bed sores that were infected. Two break-through pump drivers were inserted into his legs to keep pain medication regularly pumping into him, but the pain was still unbearable for him and for us to sit and watch. There was nothing else we could do for him, but be there, give him sips of the orange cordial he so loved, and give him a shave. Whatever dignity he had left, he handled it with grace and bravery.

We were so grateful for each minute we got to spend with Pete. We celebrated our four-year wedding anniversary on February 26. I was lying next to him in the hospital bed, sobbing and grieving for the life we had together being cut short. He held me in his weak arms and frail, failing body and said, 'It's OK babe, you and little man will be

OK. I love you more than world,' (his saying to me since we first met). One month to that day, on the 26th of March 2010 at 8.32am Pete died. He was just 31 years young, and his son was just 16 months old. Finding peace with death, knowing God was there to greet him on the other side and that the pain would be gone, helped him to let go and say goodbye.

Peter Selig. Last photograph

## Reflections

The shock of the diagnosis when Pete's melanoma returned was culminated by the fact that there were not a lot of treatment options available at the time and we knew that metastatic melanoma was a death sentence. Despite the reality, we held on to little glimmers of hope, especially when the BRAF trial was working.

In the end, as harsh and cruel as the reality was, we had hope that

Pete was no longer in pain. Hope knowing that he had made peace with death and was ready to go. Hope knowing that he knew how much he was loved and how Koby would always grow up learning and knowing how much his dad truly was one in a million.

We learned that life is a gift. It truly is so precious. When you are witnessing your loved one staring their mortality in the face, it takes all the petty things in life away. Each minute with each other was just so valuable and so precious. We remain grateful for the time that Pete enjoyed with his son, Koby. He got to witness Koby's first steps and spent every minute with him that he could – such joyous moments in the most painful of circumstances.

We honour Pete by releasing balloons on his birthday, eating his favourite foods like meatballs in tomato soup, chocolate coconut slice, mashed potato, chocolate self-saucing pudding and spinach and ricotta cannelloni. I listen to Pete's CDs and some of his favourite songs. It was incredibly painful to do for a while, but now I find it more peaceful, and it enables me to feel really connected to Pete. Most of all, we talk about Pete to Koby and keep his memory alive with his family and friends.

Being asked by Jay to contribute to this book is probably one of the most honourable ways in which we can remember Pete. It's important to know that a small piece of him is out there in the world through this book and his story. Even if Pete's outcome was the ultimate price, we hope that his story is still one of survival. We survived as a family, Pete knew how important he was and how loved he was, and Pete's memory lives on.

Jay was diagnosed with melanoma not long after Pete was diagnosed. We saw him on RPA with Janine. We got in touch with Jay as he had just started a melanoma patient support group – there was nothing else around then to support patients and their families. Jay is nothing but an inspiration to our family. He has supported us, and we have supported him in everything that he has achieved and done in the fight against melanoma. He is a humble man who will never give up! He truly has been put on this earth to make a difference to the people and families who have been affected by melanoma. If Pete had survived his journey, he would be right beside Jay doing as much as possible to save lives and to promote the research that has come so far but still has such a long way to go.

As for Koby, he is turning into a fine young man and is truly like Pete in so many ways.

#sadlymissedlovedbyall

Tony Ryan

# Tony Ryan

*by Renata Ryan (wife) and Kim Barton (daughter)*

## Renata's story

Tony was our world and melanoma is such a cruel disease. If only he had been diagnosed earlier maybe he could still have been with us today. Please have a skin check. It might just save your life!

Tony's friends and family meant the world to him and he was equally adored by them: wife Renata, daughters Kim and Tanya, son Richard, and their partners Michael, Allen and Karen; grandchildren Tarlie, Nikiya, Jack, Natalee and Justin; and great-grandchildren Tyler and Charlee. Another five great-grandchildren have been born since Tony's passing.

Tony would do absolutely anything to help anyone. He loved life and always enjoyed having a great time! He would dance the night away at parties and enjoyed water skiing, travelling, a barbecue in the fresh country air, and his Clydesdale horse. He could build and tinker around with anything and everything from antiques to old cars. You only had to look inside the shed to understand that he truly was a jack of all trades! He even bought an old school bus and decked it out into a mobile home to travel around Australia with me.

## A shower and a diagnosis

In December 2007, Tony asked me to dry his back after a shower. I noticed that a mole on his back had changed. Living in the village of Bowning in rural New South Wales, the closest skin doctor was a bit over an hour away in Canberra. Tony was able to get an appointment the next day. The doctor took one look at it and organised an immediate biopsy. A call later advised that it was melanoma and Tony was then referred to Sydney for treatment where Tony was diagnosed as stage 4. He was 57 years young.

Our family was an emotional wreck when we were told the news. We really did not know much about melanoma, but we sure did learn the hard way.

## A café and a legacy

At the time of Tony's diagnosis, he was in the process of building a slab hut café in the village. Tony had the roof and poles up and it was halfway to completion. Our savings had been spent on the project, which now seemed in doubt. Undeterred by his diagnosis, Tony was determined to finish building the 'Rollonin Café' (rollonincafe.net) and in December 2008 the café opened.

Tony poured his heart and soul into building, which took three years to complete. During this time, Tony and his mates sourced and gathered material to replicate local buildings from the 1800's.

Rollonin Cafe

Sheds and old houses were pulled down to gain the tin for the rustic look of the roof and bricks were gathered from local paddocks where old buildings had once stood and then cleaned one by one by hand. It was a mammoth task for anyone, let alone someone who was seriously ill.

Tony underwent multiple rounds of treatment. He was operated on several times and participated in three clinical trials. Between all of this, he would work on the café. The community nurse, Sandra, would come and check up on Tony on her way home from work. One day, she found him working on the roof and went crook at him, but he just smiled at her. The café truly kept Tony going and took his mind off what he was dealing with. After Tony's passing, I continued to manage his legacy, including his great cappuccino, but am now looking to retire.

## The cost of distance and treatment

Tony underwent treatment in Sydney, a good 3.5 hour's drive away from home. Travelling and trying to find accommodation, not to mention the cost of the scans and tests on top, added a significant burden. Sometimes an exhausting 7-hour round trip was on the cards, and Tony would often have to stay in Sydney for six weeks at a time.

Tony endured multiple operations. He had the melanoma removed from his back and lymph nodes. Twelve months after his initial diagnosis, he had another excised from under his armpit, then another from the back of his head. One then appeared in his adrenal gland necessitating yet another surgery which he struggled with the most.

Tony started his first trial in 2008 using a vaccine made from his own tumour that was injected into his melanoma to try and kill the cancerous cells. Then he went onto a BRAF trial which seemed to keep the melanoma at bay for a short time. When it started to come back, he was recommended for a combined BRAF/MEK drug trial but needed to wait two months before he could commence the new trial. By the time the two months was up, sadly the melanoma had spread. Tony was started on the combined trial, but it was unsuccessful. It was an emotional rollercoaster of hope followed by devastation when each treatment failed.

Throughout this time, Tony suffered through the side effects of treatment. Then, in early 2012, he was advised that there were no further options apart from trying a drug with perhaps a 20% response rate that came at a cost of $250,000. The family wanted to try and pull some finances together, but Tony refused and said that he had had enough. From that day, Tony lived for approximately another six months. He was 61 years of age.

---

It is hard to think they put a dollar value on someone's life.

---

## Kim's reflections

I love and adore my beautiful Dad who we all miss every single day.

To someone going through this, remain strong, stay positive and ask for help and support. I truly believe the treatment is getting better, so never give up hope and keep on fighting until you cannot keep up the fight any longer!

To someone supporting a loved one, support them in any way you can. Spend as much time as you can with your loved one, have no regrets and reach out to a support group.

Unfortunately, Dad really suffered during his last twelve or so months. The suffering of terminally ill people is something that really needs to be addressed. No human should have to suffer or endure what Dad did. Euthanasia/assisted dying is a tough but important discussion. My wish is that terminally ill patients with no further options have the right to end their life regardless of the State or Territory they live in. Everyone deserves to die with dignity. The suffering of the loved one, and for those surrounding the loved one, is just cruel. Had he been offered the choice, Dad would certainly have taken up the opportunity to not prolong his suffering.

He remains my hero forever and always.

## Renata's reflections (support from Jay and remembering Tony)

The biggest support my family received after Tony's passing was from the Melanoma Man (Jay Allen). He was a stranger to us all until we contacted him to see if he would be interested in being a guest speaker for our café's country fair. He kindly accepted, and we have been great friends with Jay ever since. He has built a wonderful tight-knit community that is tragically united due to melanoma.

My children, Richard and Kim, signed up to participate in one of Jay's walks in 2017 and again in May 2019 to honour their father and to help raise awareness and funds for research. My niece, Leanne, also joined them on the last walk. As Tony had always said, 'If the trial doesn't help me, it could hopefully help someone else,' so we do our bit to hopefully help others.

Tony is always talked about and we always remember the wonderful times we had together. As his wife, I feel that even though Tony is no longer with us, he lives on in our children's and grandchildren's lives. He had a beautiful smile and laugh and was a hard-working and incredible family man and friend.

Tony and Renata

Tas and Mandy Smethurst

# Tas Smethurst

*by Mandy Smethurst*

---

Tas was diagnosed with melanoma at age 48. The disease took him at the tender age of 52.

---

Tas was a quiet man. He lived simply. Nothing was ever a problem for him, and he never made a fuss about anything. He was very laid back and considered in his approach to most things in life. He was very personable and loved to help others.

We bought a farm and moved to Werai in the Southern Highlands of New South Wales in the 90's. Tas joined the Moss Vale Hockey Club to try and meet people. He also started his own lawn mowing and garden maintenance business on top of his sports photography work. He would travel all over the state taking photos of hockey tournaments. The age of digital photography and the arrival of our youngest daughter, Georgia, put a stop to that business as Tas much preferred to stay at home with the family rather than spend most weekends away during the hockey season.

After a small incident with a grass fire on our farm, Tas became a member and was then captain of the local Exeter Rural Fire Brigade for many years. He enjoyed the camaraderie of the Brigade as it was his little escape from work and family. Needless to say, Tas was very well known in the community

After a major drought, work in the lawn mowing business slowed right down. Being entrepreneurial, Tas tried to think of ways that the farm could pay for itself and he came up with the idea to establish a nursery with an on-site cafe. He poured everything into this business and, in 2009, we opened the Werai Teahouse and Nursery. Tas was in his element! He became a very good barista and loved the daily interaction with customers. He also loved gardening and created a beautiful garden for us. He grew the most stunning roses, and whilst he wasn't romantic at all, I would often find a rose in a vase next to my bed.

---

Tas was much loved by all who knew him.

---

## Man's best friend

Always by Tas's side was his best mate Chester, the Jack Russell. Chester went everywhere with Tas and everyone knew him too. Chester really wasn't that interested in anyone else in the family. He was always Tas's dog even though we all loved him dearly. He was a great little dog. Chester was aware that Tas was not well and when Tas was hospitalised towards the end of his life, Chester stopped eating and became very depressed. We got permission to take him into the hospital and after a couple of visits he came good. It was as if he knew what was happening and he was happy to be able to see his best mate and say goodbye. After Tas's death, Chester stuck to me like glue. He knew I needed him, and I like to think he needed me too. Just weeks after Tas passed away, Chester was diagnosed with thyroid cancer and only given months to live. He went on to survive for two more years. He was an amazing little dog, and so many people were saddened by his passing.

## The diagnosis

Tas first showed me a spot on the back of his knee that looked like a pimple. I told him to leave it alone and that it would go away, but it didn't. A couple of months later, Tas asked his doctor about it. The doctor thought that it was a cyst and referred him to a specialist. The specialist agreed and said he would remove it. Due to Christmas and the doctor taking leave, Tas's surgery was scheduled to happen some six or so weeks later. Two weeks before the date, the lump became very large and painful and turned a horrible purple colour. When it was finally removed, the surgeon still felt that it was just a cyst but sent it away for pathology. A week later, he delivered the news that it was a very large melanoma.

We were completely shocked by the diagnosis. Tas hated the sun. He hardly ever wore shorts and never stepped outside without blockout on and a broad brimmed hat. We could not work out how he managed to get melanoma. Telling our daughters was the hardest thing. At that time, there was an advertisement on television for melanoma that featured Wes Bonney, a young man who had died from the disease. We felt as if that ad was on TV during every ad break. It was very hard knowing that our girls were watching, and we were so unsure of what the future held. We couldn't tell them that their dad was going to be okay because we didn't know.

Tas was referred to a specialist centre and we saw him the following week. He underwent many tests on the day of his consultation, and the next day a professor performed surgery on Tas's leg to remove more tissue from the primary site. He was monitored very closely from then on. Nine months later, further tests revealed tumours in his lungs, neck, and thigh. He had radiation on his neck which destroyed the taste buds on his tongue, and while things did improve, he always said that nothing tasted the same, especially beer. Tas underwent more tests on his primary melanoma site and on the lymph nodes in his leg to see what additional treatment options were available.

We were told that Tas had a certain gene in his melanoma that responded to treatment. It was like winning the lottery as it meant that Tas could be included in a clinical trial. We were extremely happy and relieved that the trial was even possible. Being able to help the research was so important to Tas, and he was thrilled when told that the scientists had been able to grow his original melanoma and needed more blood for their research.

---

Tas knew how important the research was, and even though he often felt so unwell, he never once considered giving up.

---

Tas was put on a drug that had quite severe side effects, and it took him some time to get used to it. He could not expose any of his skin to sunlight as he would blister instantly if he did. He had nausea quite regularly and would often have a high temperature. The drug worked for 22 months before three tumours were discovered in Tas's brain. We both knew that there were no drugs at that time that worked on brain metastasis. These tumours would claim Tas's life some nine months later.

We held his funeral in his beautiful garden.

## Learning and living with hope

We lived with hope constantly. Tas was so positive throughout his entire journey. We could see that improvements in treatments were being made all the time and hoped that the research would always be a step ahead of us. It was very difficult for me to have flat days when Tas was always so positive. If you have recently been diagnosed with melanoma, Tas would tell you to never give up hope, to find a good health team, and to put your faith in them.

We also learnt so much. We learnt an incredible amount about how melanoma grows and spreads. We learnt about clinical trials, how drug companies and scientists work hard to develop new drugs, and how they finally become accessible.

We also learnt that we lived in a wonderful community that supported us so much and that included Jay Allen. Jay was always there to help in any way he could. He came and mowed our lawn, would come to appointments with us, or visit Tas when he was in hospital. He would call Tas who would just enjoy the chat on the phone. Knowing someone was thinking of him meant so much. His support and friendship were, and still are, invaluable.

Throughout the experience, I truly learnt what a courageous man Tas was. He was so strong and determined. He always said melanoma was never going to win, and he fought hard until the very end.

## Remembering Tas

Tas was very passionate about raising awareness about melanoma and assisting with research to try and prevent other people from having to go through what he was going through. I try to support awareness campaigns as I know that it is what Tas would have wanted. He felt very strongly that education was key and would have loved to have seen an education syllabus introduced into schools.

Tas would no doubt like to be remembered as a top bloke! He was a genuinely nice person who was everyone's friend, as well as a wonderful husband and father. We speak of him often and he is still very much a part of all our lives. My rose garden always reminds me of Tas, and I love spending time in it. The time we spent together running our teahouse puts a smile on my face, as do our children. Our lives go on and Tas's memory remains forever present.

Smethurst family picture | image by Alexander S Howen

Grant Lawrence (r) with Darryl Lawrence at Union Hotel, Sydney 2016, after Grant had been given the all-clear | image: Jay Allen

# Grant Lawrence

I want anyone going through something similar to know that there are people out there who have beaten the odds and overcome the diagnosis.

I like relaxing and watching sport on TV, spending time with family and friends, and playing bowls. I had been working at a resort in Coffs Harbour on the coast of New South Wales for over 10 years until I recently resigned. I'm currently senior vice president of the men's section of the Nambucca Bowls Club in New South Wales and enjoy helping at the club. I used to play a lot of soccer, AFL, cricket, and tennis when I was younger. I think my personality is pretty laid back and outgoing, but my nickname at the bowling club is 'Angry' because most people would say I go off like a firecracker when I get upset and annoyed. I admit to having no patience! I love people I get along with, but it is a different story with those I don't take to. I call a spade a spade, but I think I am sincere and kind.

I hate people who aren't honest or who think that they are better than others. I also hate snakes and spiders, waiting and doing nothing. I hate cancer, which first affected me at age 26, even more.

Growing up and family life was probably about as good as anyone could hope for. I have one older brother and we were both very spoilt. Mum and Dad were school teachers and both were highly respected. Dad was head teacher of human society and its environment (HSIE) and Mum taught food technology, textiles and design, community and family studies, and that sort of stuff. When I was growing up, we used to go camping for a couple of weeks every Christmas which was so much fun and created great memories. We also used to go to Noosa a fair bit, and I absolutely love that place. Noosaville is probably my most favourite place.

I am very close with Mum, Dad and my brother. I used to race greyhounds with Dad which Mum didn't like. We also used to play a lot of lawn bowls together and were both reasonably good, playing in the top grade for Nambucca. We loved to watch sport and yell at the footy together or with each other. Dad was extremely smart and had a wealth of knowledge and experience.

## Bowled over by melanoma

My initial melanoma was detected in August 2014. I had gone to the local GP earlier in November 2013 about a small pinkish lump on my shoulder which he said was nothing. In March 2014, I went back as it had become slightly bigger. The GP decided to do a biopsy and it returned a negative result. I went back to the medical practice within a few months and saw yet another GP as the scar from the biopsy was changing – I was given antibiotics and a cream. In August 2014, I went back to the GP again as the scar was still changing and was sent for a needle biopsy which confirmed melanoma. I was referred to a treatment centre in Sydney and scans there revealed that it had also spread to some lymph nodes under my left arm. I was stage 3.

---

The diagnosis was absolutely devastating and gut wrenching. I went from being like most 26-year-olds with the world at my feet and thinking I was bulletproof to potentially being in a fight for my life. We were all very anxious, and I was very pissed off.

---

My initial treatment at this point was a wide excision of the area on my shoulder – about a cricket ball size was cut out. I also underwent an axillary lymph node dissection to remove the lymph nodes under my left armpit and just below. I had a skin graft from my thigh to replace the piece they cut out of my shoulder. It was very painful for the first few months as I had about 60 staples to the surgical site on my shoulder and about another 60 where they took out the lymph nodes. The site where the skin was taken for the graft stung a lot and felt like someone had got a cheese grater and slid it across my thigh.

I then underwent four weeks of radiotherapy. It started off fine, but after about two and a half weeks I became very tired, and it felt like I was swallowing broken glass or razor blades. I held on to hope that it would target any rogue cells and that at the end of it I would be cancer free and able to get back on with life.

## Stage 4

Things, however, took a turn for the worse. I had not been feeling well following radiation therapy and was booked in for a follow-up appointment with an oncologist in Coffs Harbour. I was admitted to hospital and scans discovered that the melanoma had spread and was now on my liver, lungs and spine. It was February 2015, and I was now stage 4.

Being diagnosed with stage 4 melanoma was harder psychologically. As far as I was concerned, I had just finished radio-therapy, the melanoma was gone, and life was moving forward. The news itself felt like life was about to end and I was speechless – something highly unusual for me! Mum and Dad were with me and we just cried. I pretty much lost all hope and the uncertainty that came with the news was horrendous.

---

I was only 27 and had the most aggressive and deadliest skin cancer in the world. I wondered if I would be around to see my nephews grow up and whether it would be my last Christmas and birthday.

---

My treatment for stage 4 consisted of a few doses of ipilimumab followed by pembrolizumab – both types of immunotherapy. I experienced a fair bit of nausea for about the first four months and often vomited whenever I would travel anywhere, even if it was only for a few minutes. Then things became easier. I would feel tired for a couple of days after each treatment but be OK afterwards. I continued with pembrolizumab for a total of 31 months. I was also given another week of radiotherapy to try and relieve the pressure the melanoma was putting on the base of my spine and the nerves.

## Scanxiety brings hope

'Scanxiety' is a term every cancer patient will be familiar with and for good reason. Waiting to hear the oncologist call you into the office to deliver the results of the latest round of scans is tough. You just go all numb and empty and take a deep breath and you hope. Fortunately, my scans started to show positive results to the point where my oncologist said that they were 'terrific.' The treatment was working, which gave me a huge boost and lifted my spirits.

I quite often wondered whether I was going to survive and whether anyone had been through something similar, or was I just the unlucky one? That's when my oncologist and clinical nurse put me in contact with Jay Allen. The friendship I developed with Jay and the support he provided also helped significantly. We still talk or send messages nearly every day, even if it is just to put crap on each other! Every three weeks when I went to Sydney, Jay would make time to catch up with me for a drink and a chat. I thought, 'If Jay can beat this then why can't I?' Understanding the work Jay has done since his diagnosis is truly inspirational. The amount of people he has helped and the lives that he has touched is incredible. Jay is a very selfless individual and is extremely passionate about beating melanoma, as evidenced by the walks he has done and the amount of money he has raised for research.

## Reflections

I was very lucky in that Mum and Dad are both very positive people and got me through a lot of my battle with melanoma. They had both retired from teaching a couple of years prior to my diagnosis and gave up a lot of their time to take me to Sydney every three weeks for three years. They gave up years of their own lives to help me beat melanoma.

My advice to someone who may find themselves in the same position is to always try and remain positive and to look for the good. Do not worry about the small stuff and the bullshit of everyday life. If you feel weighed down, upset or whatever, then take a deep breath and think about what you have in life and find the positive. It is also very important to have a clear mind as the mind is the most powerful thing in the world. I would also advise surrounding yourself with family or good people who make you happy because you don't have the time or energy to waste on negativity. You need to have a great medical team and have confidence in the doctors and nurses as they are the experts, not the stuff you find on Google. Finally, back your gut instinct. If something doesn't feel right, then get a second and third opinion. It is also very important to know your body so that you can notice if there are any changes.

---

You always have something to be grateful for in life and there are always people worse off.

---

Today, my hopes are probably like most people – to win lotto and never have to work again! In all honesty though, I would like to see a cure for all cancers or, at the very least, a much better survival rate and quality of life for those diagnosed. Cancer has impacted my family's life in a massive and unforgiving way. Unfortunately, it continues to do so for many others.

Herman and Michelle. A special photo taken in Southern Italy in 2014, six weeks before Herman passed. He was enjoying life and living it to the most right up until the end

# Herman Herlaar

*By Michelle Meredith-Herlaar and Emily Hawrylko*

Herman wanted people to know there's others out there with melanoma. He wanted to encourage people to share their journey – the good bad and ugly …

Herman was a typical European. A charismatic man with an enormous smile and the best hugs. He was a devoted family man with four loving girls and one stepson. Herman loved love and cherished his time with all his family dearly. Weekly family dinners at home in North Lakes, north of Brisbane, were a necessity as he loved to cook, and these moments created lots of laughs. He was not a fan of mess, and this would often lead to some firm chats about the state of the kids' rooms! Herman was also a practical joker, a keen photographer and fisherman, a loyal friend and someone who loved to travel and explore. He had a gift in his ability to network and communicate with people and this would serve him well throughout his melanoma experience.

## Diagnosis

Herman's journey with melanoma was very typical of anyone living in the Sunshine State of Queensland. He loved, as we all do, being outside in the sun. Herman used sunscreen but often forgot about his back. Over a period of five months in 2004, Herman had return visits to the GP because there was something unusual on his back. Finally, the GP agreed to do a biopsy and the results were literally life changing.

Herman had his lymph nodes removed from his left armpit and the melanoma excised from his back. No other treatment seemed to be available or offered at that stage, nor were there really any support networks. The information we received was very generalised, which caused a lot of frustration, and was very scary for Herman and us all. The unknown was always the hardest part.

In 2010, Herman featured alongside other cancer survivors in a news article. Unfortunately, the melanoma did return with a vengeance. In 2014, he had his T3 and T4 vertebrae removed from his spine and these were replaced with cement and two metal rods. Herman then received stereotactic radiation to his spine, and six months later he was granted permission to take part in an immunotherapy trial.

---

Upon diagnosis, my first thoughts were: will this disease take me, or will I survive? And if I survive, what will I do to change? Will I change my diet, or will I just live my life as though my melanoma never happened? My decision was to embrace life and seek out ways of reducing the impact of this disease on others by sharing and caring. Am I brave enough to say that I am cured, in remission, or is this cancer sitting somewhere in my body just waiting for a moment of weakness? I can't answer that question. But one thing I do know is I won't allow it to control my life.

---

## Advocacy and support

Herman remained true to his word in seeking out ways of reducing the impact of melanoma on others. He became the national melanoma patient advocate and was influential in the melanoma patient community. He was instrumental in bringing about change to the red tape and timelines faced by pharmaceutical companies to release drug trials into Australia. He was not afraid of asking politicians the hard questions on why funding had been cut for melanoma research. He would always know in a crowded room who to introduce himself to. He would discuss melanoma and share his journey, and sometimes these connections would lead to more support and better outcomes for other patients. Networking was his forte. Over the years, his work in the melanoma support community touched so many families. He supported 27 people through their experience and tragic passing, and he did this with integrity and honour. The families of these people will never forget the work Herman did and he was always there no matter the time, day or night.

## An extended life

Having access to the immunotherapy trial gave Herman another 11 months of life. Within 24 hours of administration, the masses in his body had begun to reduce in size and it was simply incredible! Hope was Herman's main ethos. He held onto hope 24/7 as without it what time he had left was pretty hard. He was elated to be able to obtain the immunotherapy drug, but he was also very aware that there were others he was supporting at the time who were not as fortunate.

Herman passed away, wanting only to be remembered as a family man, on July 20, 2014. He was 54 years young.

Herman's legacy to the melanoma community extends through Jay Allen. Jay is a close friend of the family and we cherish him dearly. Herman met Jay when Jay was first diagnosed with melanoma. Herman was Jay's support person and they quickly forged a strong connection and considered each other to be brothers.

Herman was so proud to mentor and support Jay on his journey. The week Herm passed, Jay and Herm had a brother-to-brother conversation. Jay was proud to say that he would absolutely continue to support patients on their melanoma journey just as Herman had mentored him to do. Emily (Herm's daughter) is a close friend of Jay and has maintained our family's support by walking with Jay during the Brisbane – Melbourne walk in 2017 where they shared happy memories of Herman.

## Words of wisdom

Herman had many words of wisdom. He always made sure you knew that you were loved so dearly by him. His unconditional love for life was incredible and continues to inspire us every day.

Every single moment of each day needs to be treasured. Tell your loved ones how much you care for them. Any negative influence was removed from our world. We embraced love and happiness as each moment we were given together was a blessing. We always made sure, when Herman was not well enough to speak or understand the conversations, that there was a loved one with him, a voice to speak on his behalf.

Listen to your body, challenge the doctors, research your possible treatments holistically, and reach out for support from others who have been on a similar journey. Talk to your friends and cherish each day. Herman would encourage you to Get Naked With Your Loved One once a week. Check each other's body and keep an eye on anything that might change. Prevention and awareness can lead to better outcomes.

Herm would have wished that one day we could live with melanoma like we do with other diseases and not die from it. Only with research, funding and drug trials will this be possible in the future.

Herman and Michelle

Australia Skin Cancer Foundation Skin Check Truck

https://www.australianskincancerfoundation.org/skin-check-truck

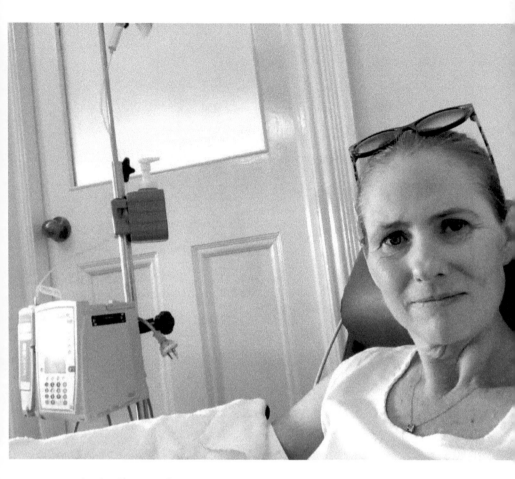

Louise Sherwood

# Louise Sherwood

When I relapsed, I'd had the opportunity to follow stories and understand the advances in treatment and that gave me so much hope. I want to provide hope for others ...

I grew up in Manly, Sydney, New South Wales, with my mum (Jill), my dad (Mike), my sister (Leonora, who we call Leo) and my brother (Adam). I still live in Sydney. I married Rob in 2014, have a three-year-old daughter (Indiana), and am step-mum to a 16-year-old girl (Zara). The family has grown significantly with an extra 19 people on my husband's side and 10 on my side, which makes for wonderful family get-togethers! Part of the family is also my very fluffy Birman cat, Cleopatra, who truly is an aloof princess. She sleeps most of the day and hunts the house at night for insects to torment.

I consider myself outgoing with a genuine interest in people. I don't like rudeness and selfishness and go out of my way to help those in need. My husband would describe me as definitely grumpy before my morning coffee, but happy, bubbly, and ready to tackle the day once the caffeine takes hold! He also thinks that I find things extra amusing after a couple of wines! I love cooking up a storm and entertaining, and my happy place would be in a restaurant with my favourite people eating good food and chatting! I am not particularly sporty but try to get to the gym a few times a week, have learned to play amateur golf, and don't mind a dip in the ocean or a long beach walk.

My early career was as a travel agent selling holidays specifically to Queensland. I did a variety of other jobs after that, but the longest part of my working life so far has been in investment banking IT running large scale software delivery projects. I stopped working in 2015 to start a degree in primary school teaching, but this was put on hold when my daughter was born in July 2017, which also coincided with my latest diagnosis.

93

# Diagnosis

I was living in London when I was diagnosed with melanoma. Around the end of 2009, I remember waking up one morning with a funny pink pimple-looking thing on my cheek, but I knew it was different to a pimple. I went straight to a GP who referred me to a dermatologist to check this 'new mole'. The dermatologist said it was likely a cyst and that if I cut it out, I would have a scar. As a single 33-year-old, a scar on my face was the last thing I wanted and so I decided to leave it. It actually started to go away, but this took months.

---

My doctor was even bold enough to say, 'There's no need to be so upset. It's not like you have melanoma.'

---

Fast forward about nine months and I discovered a pea-sized lump by my ear near where the so-called cyst had been. In September 2010, I travelled home to Sydney for a friends' wedding and took the opportunity to visit my family GP who told me I had a blocked lymph node and, once again, to not worry! In 2011, I was offered a position in New York, so in May I took off on a whirlwind trip around the world in preparation for the big move and the long spell before there would be another break. The last stop on my trip was Sydney to see my family.

I happened to tell my sister on the way back to the airport that I had this lump and that it had grown a bit despite being told it was nothing. She suggested that I seek a second opinion. I arrived back in London and went back to work only to be asked to leave for New York the following day. I told my boss that I needed to get something checked out before I could leave.

The second opinion instantly referred me to a head and neck specialist who told me I had a tumour but that it was most likely benign. He did three biopsies, all of which were inconclusive, but what they did reveal without doubt was the presence of cancer. I remember feeling so upset hearing those words, but the type of cancer they were suggesting was very slow growing and the one that everyone wanted if they had to get cancer.

# Surgery

In late May of 2011, I underwent considerable surgery to remove my parotid gland (salivary gland) and the tumour. My older sister, Leo, flew over from Australia to help with my recovery as I had nerve damage to my face. I really want to highlight this time with her. We were only a year apart in age, had not lived in the same country for many years; but she was my rock. We had a wonderful week together that bought us even closer. It was a week we could never have planned because of the pressures of family but under emergency circumstances we made the most of it. Leo had planned to stay until after the pathology results came in, but they were delayed. She left London the night before I finally saw my doctor and flew to Bermuda where my brother and sister-in-law were living and had just had their first baby. This should have been Adam and Natasha's time – they had lived away from family for nearly 10 years in Bermuda and were so excited about the arrival of their first child. Her birth coincided with my diagnosis which shifted a lot of the focus onto me.

---

My brother and his wife should have been basking in all the fuss associated with the arrival of a first child, but I took the limelight for reasons I would never wish on anyone.

---

I received the news that it was melanoma and that it was secondary – it had spread. I called Leo and my brother and gave them my credit card and just said, 'I need someone with me.' I knew Leo needed to get back to her kids, and Adam had a new baby, but I begged, 'Whatever it costs, please just come back.' It was heart-breaking for all.

The very next morning, I was sent for a PET scan. Leo had flown overnight from Bermuda and was in the waiting room when I came out of the scan. We both burst into tears. We were wrecked. We left with my friends Rachel and Cath and went straight in to see a melanoma oncologist. I instantly became the patient who always had three or four friends or family with her as no-one could bare to not be there to hear what was going on. I was thrown head-first into a

95

frightening and confronting new world. My PET was thankfully clear. My oncologist reminded me that it was still curable at stage 3 but wanted me to undergo more surgery to remove the lymph nodes in my neck to make sure that there had not been any further spread.

---

**I felt like I was on a treadmill that was going downhill at full speed.**

---

The mental and physical turmoil was immense. Surgery was scheduled and yet I had only just healed from the previous effort and still had significant nerve damage to my face. My sister stayed until just before the surgery. I attended many appointments – some to look for the primary tumour and others to check my recovery. We stumbled across the Helen Reddy song, 'I am woman', which is not generally my taste in music, but the words made us feel strong: *We had wisdom born of pain. Yes, I've paid a price but look how much I've gained. I can do anything, I am strong, I am invincible ...* 'It became our anthem and one I continue to hold onto.

Outside the ongoing appointments, Leo and I shopped when I could (albeit bandaged up), laughed, cried, and curled up in front of movies. I have one memory of feeling very anxious and Leo made me try meditation. She played a guided meditation CD and we lay on the floor. Ironically, it started off by telling us to imagine we were lying on a deserted beach. All I could think was that it was the bloody beaches that put me in this situation and that I did not put any sun cream on! Leo immersed herself into my London life for a week and saw how much love and support I had around me. Even though my flat mate was not there a lot of the time, Leo chose to share my bed. I was so lucky to have a sister. The overall memory of that time is wonderful.

As Leo left London to go home, Mum and Dad flew out from Sydney to take over. I had to ask my beautiful friend (SJ) to temporarily move out so that my parents could stay. They arrived just before my next surgery that saw me emerge looking like something from a horror film. My neck had been cut open and stapled back together and, from that moment, the movement and feelings in my neck would never be the same.

My neck dissection was thankfully clear, and I headed into the long healing process. My weeks blurred into a schedule of appointments. I was fortunate in that my employer was incredibly supportive until my income protection insurance took over. I needed to see an eye doctor regularly because the nerve damage meant that I could not blink – you have no idea how much you blink during the day until you no longer can! This also translated into having to wear sunglasses day and night to ward off the dust and dirt in the atmosphere that I could no longer blink away.

I started seeing a physiotherapist to try and get movement back in my face so I could eat, drink and blink properly. I also could not lift my arm straight after surgery, so even more physio was required. I had check-ups with dermatologists who were still perplexed about not being able to find the primary tumour on my skin. My oncologist saw me regularly as he wanted to put me on a trial, but that is a whole other story! My surgeon also continued to check on the progress of my recovery and it was all very full on. Despite this, I managed to have a social life as connecting with people was so important to my mental health. After any appointment, my first thought was, 'Where can we go to unwind after this?' The idea of going home and sitting in my apartment just made me feel so down. Thankfully, Dad was always willing to accommodate a trip to a local pub and was brilliant at turning any negative thought into a positive. Dad really does not like medical talk, but he said to me often during that time that 'a problem shared is a problem halved.' I realise now that I got to know my father a lot better during those times; we would chat about his life and stories that I had never heard before. Mum was always there to support us. It was not always her scene, but without a doubt she was ready to provide those much-needed hugs that only mums know how to do.

## The clinical trial that changed everything

My oncologist asked me to take part in a clinical trial for a drug called Avastin®. In my mind, I knew I did not want to take the drug and hoped that I would score the placebo arm which would still enable me to be closely monitored as a trial participant.

To start a trial, you need to first pass a wide range of checks to meet the trial's protocol requirements. My first was a baseline CT scan as you had to be clear of melanoma before you started. You can imagine my surprise when I got the call to say that my CT scan had discovered three spots on my liver. My oncologist was very reassuring. He said that as the recent PET had been clear it was more likely to be cysts, or something similar, but to be sure I needed to have an MRI that day. Dad had previously left to go to and see relatives in Dublin, and Mum and I had booked tickets to the theatre and unfortunately lost our money. The MRI was another exceptionally confronting experience. I know so many people suffer huge claustrophobia when having scans and I can completely understand why. I spent two and a half hours in the machine without any warning about how long it would take, and it all seemed so excessive. Mum and I left the hospital at about 8.00pm and headed home for a sleepless night.

I remember the call from Mum to Dad discussing whether he needed to come back to London from Dublin. She told him he needed to fly back. He was on the first flight out the next morning in time for the three of us to see the oncologist. Walking into his office was hard but the day became much harder. The first thing he said was, 'Wow, you certainly are on a roller coaster at the moment.' Much of the appointment was a blur, and I had to be sedated as I started shaking so much, but the results of the MRI confirmed that the spots were almost definitely melanoma. We were taken into another little room where the very serious discussions happened. There was a couch – you knew it was serious when it was decked out nicely – and the doctors and nurses set about planning the next steps.

I will take a detour away from the medical plan for a moment to focus on why this day is etched in my memory as being one of the worst and yet, ironically, also one of the best days of my life. I got in a cab after leaving the doctor's office with my parents and remember hearing mum say, 'Let's go home and get a cup of tea.' I said, 'No way! I need to be out and about,' so we went to a pub in London Bridge, right on the water. As it was warm in London, we sat outside. I called my support group in London: Janine, Rachel, SJ, Cath and Duncan. They all left work immediately (11.00am) and came to join us. Their partners arrived too throughout the afternoon as did other friends. It was a bittersweet day that I will never forget. We drank the best champagne, we laughed at the fact that I would be bald at Janine's wedding and what sort of wig I'd wear, we cried at the enormity of it all, and we hugged. There was so much closeness and support amongst the group that day and I could not have felt more loved. Dad still remembers that day as a contrast between wonderful and petrifying. My poor mum, who does not crave social interaction like Dad and I do, probably needed some downtime from the enormity of it all, but she laughed and cried with the rest of us. I was so pleased to have them there in my world.

## The plan for now

As circumstances change, plans on a cancer journey constantly change and you need to be prepared to adapt and alter course. My new plan was another PET scan and liver biopsy followed by very hard-core chemotherapy (which we already know does not work on melanoma). Monday morning came and I went to my PET scan and let the rest become a blur. I went to meet some friends afterwards and could not shake the feeling that the doctors were wrong – it was not cancer! I do not know if it was ignorance, intuition, or denial, but the feeling was strong. I was due to see the doctor later in the week but the very next morning I received a call from the nurse saying that my PET was clear, that the spots on my liver were not showing up as actively as they should and therefore they couldn't be melanoma. I collapsed to the floor, having just fled another incredibly scary loop on my rollercoaster. A liver biopsy was performed as a 'belts and braces' check, but the outcome of that additional stress was also clear – it was not cancer! However, a caveat was added in that I needed repeat scans in three months just to be sure. I was so burnt out by this stage that I decided to take a long break at home in Australia with my family and get some sea air, do some yoga, and have some much-needed family time. So, home to Sydney I went where I also took the opportunity to have my case reviewed by local experts. I went on to have three follow up PET scans the following year to monitor my liver and these didn't show anything that warranted any real concern.

## Moving home and new discoveries

While still in Sydney, I decided to move my life back to Australia. Just before leaving to go back to London to pack everything up, I had one last skin check. The doctor decided to biopsy a small pink mark on my cheek that had been previously discarded as anything sinister and bang – hit again by melanoma! I had to wait six weeks to have surgery to remove this unassuming mark. It was pink, not very dark, and the margins were not clear. I was devastated. I had a three centimetre in diameter circle of skin cut out of my cheek which was replaced with skin from my arm. The melanoma was in situ, which does not explain the spread, but being so close to my secondary tumour, the only reasonable explanation is that it was most likely the primary.

## Little new beginnings

A lot happened after that. I was single, 35-years-old, moving back to Australia to restart my life and scarred both mentally and physically. I put my big girl pants on and braved the world of internet dating. I could tell so many stories on that subject alone, but it did result in meeting my now husband, Rob, that very year. We met in October 2012, bought a house together the following June, and married a year later.

Rob and I both wanted to have a baby but were acutely aware of the risks after stage 3 melanoma. We ended up speaking in depth to my oncologist regularly. I was on annual PET scans and we were given the go ahead to do IVF*. It took a couple of years, but in late 2016 we were successful, and I was now five years clear. Everything was looking good. I had a scan just before the good embryo was transferred. In July 2017, my beautiful daughter Indiana was born. I was due for a PET in September, but my appointment came and went. I saw my oncologist and told her I had been too tired with a new baby to face it. She told me to do it before Christmas. The truth was that I was not feeling very well. I would have the odd day of feeling a bit nauseous and my right shoulder ached a lot. I was extremely tired but put everything down to having a tiny baby and not getting any sleep. I booked my PET for early November.

I remember the PET day clearly as the doctor asked me before the scan if I had any aches or pains. I replied that I was aching all over but that a baby explains it! I left the scan and burst into tears. I was not allowed to be around my daughter for a few hours so went to meet my sister for lunch. My phone rang while I was out with 'No caller ID' displaying on the screen. My heart stopped because my oncologist's office always showed 'No caller ID'. I was right to be nervous. My oncologist needed to speak to me and had cleared the first appointment of the day. At that point, I nearly fainted. My sister, as always, was trying to be positive but admitted she felt sick. I felt numb. I called my husband and we all met back at my house. As soon as I saw Rob, he hugged me tighter than he had ever hugged me before. I could feel his fear, but in his very stoic way he put on a brave face and told me we would deal with whatever it was the oncologist needed to tell me. All I knew at this point was that the news would not be good and that I was lucky to be married to such a strong man.

The next morning, the three of us attended the dreaded appointment where I learned my liver had lit up on the PET scan. There were four tumours. The largest measured 10x10 centimetres (cm), with the other three each measuring 4x4 cm. They were enormous! A lot of my liver was now occupied with cancer. I was in shock and looking at my baby girl who was just four months old and oblivious to what was currently happening to her mum. I could not bear the thought of her growing up without me. I was back on the rollercoaster and the speed had picked up. Those spots that were discovered six years earlier in London had sneakily lay dormant and managed to evade a correct diagnosis. Meanwhile, I had been living with stage 4 cancer but never knew it. I don't feel anger about the misdiagnosis, but I am acutely aware of how different my life would have been had the original liver spots turned out to be melanoma back in 2011. I cannot imagine life without my little family now, and the thought of not being able to have my daughter is just inconceivable. To get to where I am today, this path had to run its course and, despite everything, it is difficult to be angry at it.

## Two years

I needed another liver biopsy and another CT scan and when the results of these were in, I would be given a new treatment plan. It took two long weeks to obtain the results, which confirmed the PET scan, and I started immunotherapy straight away. I was given some scary statistics: 50% of people respond, but the liver is harder to treat so my odds of success were less. I cannot remember the exact rate quoted for my scenario but do remember my oncologist looking at me straight in the eye and saying, 'Louise, this is very serious.'

My immunotherapy consisted of ipilimumab and nivolumab, also known as ipi/nivo. I got through all four doses of the combination over 12 weeks which apparently is not common due to side effects. The main side effects I experienced from this drug combination were stomach pains and fatigue. I had been told that vitiligo (loss of pigment in skin) was a sign that the drugs were working. I looked every day at my very pale and freckly skin to see if it had changed, but each day brought nothing. On the day of my follow-up scan after treatment, my brother casually mentioned that he thought my freckles had faded. The results of this scan showed an 80% reduction in tumour size. Three months of treatment had produced an amazing response and the side effect of vitiligo – I was one very happy girl! I then spent a further two years on nivo alone.

At about 18 months into this treatment, my tumours were classified as stable on the latest scan, which had been the case for a while. Even though this was good news, I was not considered to be in the clear. It was so important to celebrate that we were winning and so that evening I had dinner with my best friend Angela and her husband Tony. At dinner, I declared that I was going to start living and believing that I was cancer-free rather than being 'stable,' despite what the doctors had said. Ironically, the next scan showed no evidence of disease! Who knows if it was intuition, but I had started to feel that I didn't need the drugs anymore and that my body was sending some very strong signals. It took nearly two years to achieve a complete metabolic response and to hear the words 'all clear.' The moment was celebrated with the whole family in Manly. How truly special it was to be able to feel free of cancer.

# Reflections

Being told you have cancer is gut wrenching to say the very least. However, I always believed I would get through my diagnosis even when the doctors said how serious it was. I think the thought of not being there for my daughter or stepdaughter just filled me with fear. I did not want my husband to do it on his own, we are a team, and I was in no way ready to bow out.

The true effect on family members is hard to know. My husband is a very practical and intelligent man who looks forward rather than looking back. Even though waiting to see if those initial three months of treatment had worked or not was hard, we remained positive and just got on with it. At night, when we lay close in bed, we wouldn't talk in depth about what may lay ahead, but I did say to him at one point, 'If this doesn't work, I really won't have much time. My liver is almost completely covered in cancer. What if they can't turn it around?' I knew he was thinking the same even though it was never verbalised.

One day during treatment, I went for a walk with my younger brother. He became a father to a little boy three months before my daughter was born so was also in the thick of things with kids. He casually said, 'You can tell me anything, Lou. It won't scare me.' I replied that the only scary thing going on in my head was that if the treatment failed, I wanted 'it' to be quick. I didn't want my daughter to feel the pain of knowing me and then losing me. My beautiful stepdaughter was in the midst of her teenage years and was very stoic, but I truly wish for her that we had not been so distracted with a baby and a very serious cancer diagnosis.

My wider family were very worried but are also sensible and intelligent people. Once there were signs that the treatment was working and we were able to give encouraging information, it calmed everyone a lot and gave them faith. I was so fortunate to have such an amazing support network. My sister insisted on being at every appointment and she came to most treatments – which were a lot. It almost became a social event every two weeks where we could have a coffee and catch up while I had my infusion. Although my sister and husband came to every appointment, my whole family and friends played an equally important role in supporting me.

My support network was expanded through Jay Allen who I met when I first returned to Sydney. I emailed him, he replied immediately and offered to meet me for a green tea at circular quay. We hit it off and he filled me with so much hope. It was so good to meet someone who really understood. Jay is always on the end of the phone if you need him and is extremely sensitive to everyone's situation. Most of all, he never shies away from the really tough stuff. If people are struggling, he holds them up. If the treatment is not working, he is by your side. The man is a legend!

I was lucky enough to walk with Jay for a couple of days on one of his walks from Adelaide to Sydney. I remember finishing the first day, having walked 18 kilometres of it. I walked alongside a girl I met who was going through the same thing, Ruby. She has become a very close friend and a partner in the melanoma journey. We met other wonderful people that day – some who had lost loved ones and another who sadly went on to lose her sister, which is something I will never forget. Jay cheered us all along, listening intently to everyone's stories with an always sympathetic and understanding ear.

## Words of hope

I finished treatment at the beginning of 2020 and have confidence that it has killed the cancer for good. I now hope to live a long and healthy life and equally hope that my family remains in good health. Whether it was denial, or an innate sensation that I would be OK, I always had very strong feelings that all would end well.

After treatment ended, I was keen to embark on a new career. My daughter was attending day care and I was hired to volunteer on a survivorship program. I wanted to help others and hoped that it would open some doors to working in a field that I was hugely passionate about. Then COVID-19 hit, putting the idea of a career change on hold.

At the time of writing, it has been almost 10 years since I was initially diagnosed with melanoma. It has been a long road and I have learned a lot. I have put any self-doubt or self-criticism aside and realised that I am too amazing to be taken off this earth just yet. I still have so much to give. This whole unfortunate experience has certainly given me more confidence. I do not worry about small things anymore.

To others battling melanoma or another type of cancer, I would say, 'Have hope, stay healthy, be positive and look forward rather than dwelling on the past.' Stay educated on treatments and trials and connect with others who are going through the same. There is a wealth of knowledge and support out there!

Finally, throughout this whole experience, I have never once thought that I would want to change what happened to me. It has been an awfully tough thing to go through, and at times the fear was so overwhelming that this line of thinking seems ridiculous. However, it did force me to change my life and gave me the opportunity to open myself up to meeting a wonderful man and his daughter. We created a new life together and deal with the challenges. I am definitely more content.

At the time of writing, I am casually studying counselling and have recently been approached for a role back in banking which I accepted. I am excited to be renewing my career within the context of a slower paced life. You see things through very different eyes when your mortality is questioned, and whilst sometimes I find that it has provided wonderful clarity, it is not something I would wish upon anyone. I am also acutely aware that not everyone's journey has worked out as successfully as mine. I remain forever grateful for medical research and for the people before me who shared their stories to give me hope. I hope that I can do the same for those who will unfortunately come after me.

*Not everyone who has received a cancer diagnosis is suitable for IVF treatment. The decision to proceed with IVF as a cancer survivor needs careful consideration and discussion with medical specialists.

Natasha Stork and Marley

# Natasha Stork

There was absolutely no indication of melanoma until I experienced severe abdominal pain three months after giving birth.

I was diagnosed with stage 4 melanoma at the age of 34. I had tumours all over my liver, stomach, small intestine and hip bone.

I am very fair skinned and spent my childhood in Melbourne enjoying the sun. I would hang around Dad as he washed the car out in the driveway under the sun, and my parents would sunbake in the backyard to get a tan. They were a bit slack with sunscreen and would encourage us to put a bit on but not enough. I was sunburned as a kid to the point where I suffered sunstroke whilst on holidays on Philip Island.

As an adult, I wanted a tan for vanity reasons. I used solariums in my early 20's quite regularly for a couple of years and throughout the year. I even used accelerator lotion before the solarium to accelerate the tan. All of this took its toll. I developed moles and freckles from being sunburned and, looking back, it is not really a surprise I wound up with melanoma.

I always thought melanoma was just skin cancer – get one, cut it out and that's the end of that! A lot of people still think like that, unfortunately. I am happy to talk about melanoma quite a lot as it is quite cathartic. I don't mind talking about it because it's just part of my life and the people I do speak to always seem surprised. They often do not realise that it can be so deadly and that sometimes it just cannot be cut out. The ads on TV still don't cut it – pardon the pun!

I married my husband Grant in 2011. His father is Sri Lankan and his mum is Australian and he is a wonderful mix of dark skin and blue eyes. We were married in the Cook Islands and I wanted to have a tanned look for the wedding, so I was still tanning right up until the big day. One of my girlfriends asked me what the one thing is that I want to be remembered for in life and I replied, 'Easy, I want to be a mum.' So, when I found out I was pregnant a few years later, it was the best news ever! I drove to the chemist to get more pregnancy tests to be sure and a 'Bob Marley' song came on which cemented the decision to call my child, if it was a girl, Marley.

## The black dot that changed everything

I was 14 weeks pregnant and had just informed my employer of my pregnancy. I had also found a spot, like a full stop made by a black pen, on the back of my arm. Ironically, my work was holding a skin check day and the verdict was that I had a lot of moles and freckles, and that the black one on the back of my arm should be looked at by a dermatologist. I had it in my head to get it checked out at some point but put it aside. I thought I might wait until after the baby was born as I did not want to do any procedures while I was pregnant.

After an uncomplicated 16-hour labour, little Marley was born. It was an exciting time and life was great! When she was eight weeks old, I decided to go and get the thing on the back of my arm checked out. I remember the timing because it was the first time I somewhat nervously left Marley alone with my husband. My GP, who was also my obstetrician, removed the offending lesion on the spot.

Within a few days, I received a call from my GP stating that she did not want to alarm me but that it was an in-situ melanoma. It was apparently 99% curable and had clear margins so everything should have been fine. However, a few weeks later, in the middle of the night while I was breast feeding Marley, I experienced quite painful cramping in my stomach area. I was not overly worried until it began to wake me in the middle of the night and was becoming worse. At a standard check-up with Marley, I raised the cramping pains. My doctor thought that the uterus might still be contracting especially as I was breastfeeding. I started doing home enemas thinking that maybe I was constipated, but it did not do the trick, and I ended up holding a water bottle across my stomach for much of the night. I went back to my doctor the same week and she sent me for an ultrasound. The sonographer took Marley out of the bassinet while he was doing the ultrasound as she was not settled. He would have known right away what was causing the pain but did not give anything away. Later that day, I received a call from my doctor's receptionist who asked me to come in at 5.30pm and to bring my husband. I told Grant and he started to freak out.

---

Being diagnosed was the worst thing any of us could have heard. Shock, disbelief, confusion, heartbreak, and overwhelming fear.

---

We arrived at an empty clinic. It was deathly quiet with no-one else there. My doctor was also very nervous and upset and it took her a while to get the message out. I was not sure what was happening or what I expected to hear, but the words, 'It's cancer,' came as a massive shock. The day was August 3, 2015. I just froze and did not react. Grant started having an anxiety attack to the point where he nearly passed out. The nurse came in to deal with him and Marley was crying. 'So, what now?' My doctor explained that my liver was covered in tumours and that it was a secondary cancer. I didn't really understand what she meant. She said, 'It's come from somewhere else …' I still did not really comprehend, but within a couple of days found myself at a treatment centre for a liver biopsy, PET scans, MRIs, and brain scans.

The endoscopy was not exactly pleasant. The anaesthetist had to rush off to surgery, so my endoscopy went ahead with only a numbing spray in my throat, and it was very uncomfortable. It found tumours on my stomach lining. The liver biopsy procedure went ahead as planned. I was unaware at the time, or perhaps I just did not realise, but I also had blood taken as part of a 'liquid biopsy' trial. These results came back quickly, and a family meeting was called. My mother-in-law, Dad, my oncologist, and his registrar attended and explained that I had advanced melanoma. The reality of what that meant, even at that point, had still not quite hit home. Leading up to that meeting, no-one knew what type of cancer it was except that it had spread and that I had a high tumour burden. Everything was then full steam ahead.

There was talk of going onto chemotherapy. A hospital dietitian came to see me for a chat about nutrition and about keeping my body weight up. I learned that there was also a new treatment, immunotherapy, that was not yet available on the PBS but due to be listed soon. I was going to receive dabrafenib and trametinib, a type of targeted therapy. Knowing that some people had managed to keep their melanoma under control for six years using this treatment gave me hope. At this time, I was still breast feeding and had intended to breast feed for a year or so as I was very lucky in that it came easy to me. I was told I would have to stop breast feeding before starting treatment which was dreadfully upsetting. I had at least managed to breast feed my beautiful Marley up to the age of 14 weeks. I spent 11 days in hospital for all the tests and scans but was not allowed to be around Marley for a day at a time due to the scans and the associated radioactivity, no matter how miniscule it was. As there was no breast pump in the hospital, my breasts became engorged and uncomfortable, but the nurses were amazing and helped me to express the milk. I was given a tablet to stop lactation and that made me really sick. I cried and cried and vomited which was a reaction to the hormone in the tablet rather than the cancer. My GP had given me her mobile number to call her anytime – she was across the whole journey – and late one night I did as we could not get Marley to take a bottle. The GP ended up referring me to the midwives at another hospital who gave me some help over the phone in the middle of the night and eventually she drank.

## The beginning of treatment

I was not involved in a true clinical trial but participated in a research registry. This involved having a PET scan three days after starting treatment and then another seven days after starting. I had a great response and the scans showed that the tumours were shrinking each time. I took the targeted therapy for seven weeks and achieved a complete response! All the tumours had gone! My aunty did not quite believe me – it was too good to be true!

After being in the clear for a month or two, it was time for another scan. Unfortunately, the tumours had popped up in my internal abdominal wall cavity and on my liver again. We had been told right at the beginning that the targeted therapy was not a cure and that the tumours would come back. So, I knew they would return but never expected it to happen quite so quickly. The tumours literally came back as fast as they had disappeared, and I have not yet met anyone else who has had the same sort of response.

In November 2015, I started pembrolizumab, a type of immunotherapy. I was warned of the side effects but did not really experience anything major. However, I developed an underactive thyroid, but it is not too bad and well-managed with thyroxine. The other main side effect, which happened within a couple of months over summer, is that my skin started to change colour. I developed white and dark patches on my hands, and these were considered a really good sign that my body was responding because the immune system was eating away at the melanin.

In mid-January 2016, I was home and eating my healthy organic food (a vegetable patty with a fried egg on top) when I developed horrible pains in my abdominal area that literally freaked me out. I asked Grant to take me to the hospital and we were both extremely scared. I had not undergone a scan since starting the immunotherapy so had no idea where things were at. I was violently ill and vomited out the side of the car on the way to the hospital. We made it into the emergency department, and I was stretchered off for a CT scan. Grant, Dad, and Marley (9 months old) were present. The doctor informed me that I needed surgery that night as I had intussusception – a tumour on the small intestine was blocking the passage of food and causing problems. Mum had previously told me to ask the right questions before consenting to going under the knife, so I asked the doctor what he would do if it was him. He looked at me like I was crazy as he knew how serious it was and added, 'If I had a nine-month-old baby, I would have the surgery!!' A small part of my small intestine, about 10 centimetres, was removed via my belly button.

The day after surgery, the surgeon came to say hello. I was alone and he said, 'We had a look around while we were in there and it looks like the treatment is working.' It was the most awesome news! I grabbed his hand and thanked him. I recovered well despite the morphine making me feel sick and, boosted by the positive news, only spent a few days in hospital. Friends and family came to visit and gave me things that were easy to eat and drink. The hospital food was not the best but being close to a bunch of good restaurants helped.

## The road to freedom

I was not allowed to lift Marley for about six weeks which made things hard at home. In March 2016, after recovering from surgery, I went in for my three-month immunotherapy follow-up scan and was eager for positive news given what the surgeon had said a few weeks earlier. I spoke to my oncologist after the scan and he confirmed that all the tumours had gone except for one which was new and located on my spleen. I did not have any pain or issues and so we gave it a bit more time to respond. Unfortunately, it decided to do otherwise and kept on growing, despite everything else being fine. The time came to take it out!

I was booked in for surgery on May 31, 2016. I was prepared and excited as it was the last tumour, and it was about to be removed. I was looking for those three elusive letters to be written against my file: NED – no evidence of disease. I woke up in recovery and was then transferred to the ward. I was still doped-out when the surgeon came in with some trainees and said that he had not removed the tumour as it was deeper than they expected. I was incredibly upset and rang Grant. He was angry that I had received this news while alone and still half out of it. We found out that when the surgeons went to remove the tumour on the spleen that they had seen more tumours in the abdominal wall cavity and liver. They called the oncologist who had said 'no' during surgery as there was no point in putting me through a big operation when new tumours were developing.

A biopsy of the new tumours was taken while I was on the operating table. It was a long three days before the results came through. We were waiting and preparing for the worst-case scenario and contemplating what other options might be available. The results were somewhat unexpected – the tumours were old tumours and scar tissue, and with this brought such massive relief! The surgeons had thought that the lesions were new melanomas because they were black, but it was just left-over scar tissue from the old tumours. I was subsequently booked back for my original spleen surgery, but as it

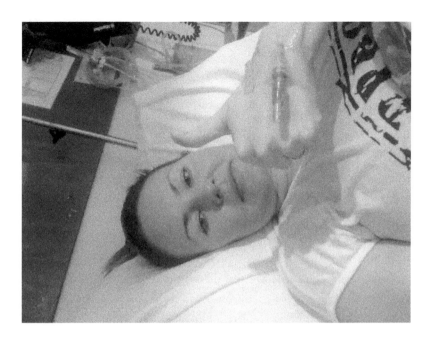

Natasha Stork

could not be achieved via the belly button I ended up with a large incision and a splenectomy, together with the removal of a slither of my pancreas and stomach, to get clear margins. The head surgeon came in and said, 'We got it,' and informed me that they had also found that I have an accessory spleen – a little baby spleen that might take on some of the work of the excised spleen. The day was June 3, 2016, and it is the day I consider my 'cancer free birthday.'

---

In less than one year I beat cancer!

---

The recommendation for me was to remain on immunotherapy every three weeks for two years. I was so lucky in that I responded so well with no major side effects. Every treatment day became a 'treat' day and something to look forward to, and so after treatment it would be off to the fish and chip shop not far from the hospital.

I stopped immunotherapy in November 2017. I continued to have three-monthly scans for a while, then six-monthly, and the last one was in December 2020 at a 12-month point. I am now officially discharged from the cancer unit and do not need to return, but I've decided to have another scan in December 2021.

## Giving back

I feel emotional talking about what happened to me but at the same time I like talking about it. I want to be able to help people. I remember telling my oncologist that I wanted to be able to give back. I helped at the hospital for a while but finally it reached a point where I wanted to take a break from it all. I really try now to educate people just in conversation – from someone I might meet through work or socially. It tends to come up at some point providing an opportunity to talk about melanoma and good health. I feel that this was all supposed to happen and that I am on the path I am supposed to be on. In a strange way, it has been a gift, and by no means do I intend that remark to be offensive to people who have lost loved ones. This cancer is horrid and takes far too many people and should never be downplayed, but for me, in its own way, it has been a gift because I am happier and have found my path in life.

I now have a strong interest in health and wellbeing, spurred on by personal experience. I began to take care of myself – even more so after my diagnosis – to keep my immune system as strong as possible. I firmly believe that by keeping my immune system strong I will be fine. I cut out red meat, refined sugar, alcohol, and coffee and continue to feed myself good food, eating organically whenever possible. I do not feel that I am depriving myself and it has not been difficult. I see it as my way of taking back some control to help my body help itself, but I am not advocating that it is a proven science or that it is for everyone.

I also started a small business making my own wellness products containing magnesium, an essential mineral for our bodies*. I found that magnesium oil baths helped me to relax and aided my joint pain from the targeted therapy, and I am keen to share this with others. Having worked in a stressful call centre, I changed jobs after having found my new path in life and now also work at an organic food store.

I have made a lot of friends who are going through melanoma

thanks to Jay. He is a hero, a beacon of hope and a true leader to our community.

My message to others going through this is to develop a positive mindset, take your health into your own hands, and keep your immune system as strong as possible.

## *MarleyGrace Magnesium

Facebook: www.facebook.com/marleygracemagnesium/
Instagram: www.instagram.com/marleygracemagnesium/
Facebook blog: My Road to Wholesome Health

The information and views contained within are Natasha's personal views and are not intended to replace the advice of a suitably qualified medical practitioner.

---

You are strong, but you do not know how strong you are until you have no choice.

---

Ruth Davey

# Ruth Davey

I'm sharing for others to realise how important it is to check yourself and others for changes to your skin. No person ever deserves to suffer like some of us have when the message is out there to be sun and skin safe.

Family has always been my priority. I love children and have raised five girls on the central coast of New South Wales – three of my own and two from my husband's first marriage. I cherish them all dearly. I have worn many hats in my working life – sales assistant then manager, childcare, office jobs and even picking fruit. I did what I could so long as it fitted into my children's lives.

I am a big fan of animals of all kinds, but especially cats, and wish others would care for and love animals unconditionally. Being kind isn't hard and it makes you feel good. I also love singing and mending items or knitting and crocheting.

Prior to my melanoma diagnosis in October 2010 at the age of 46 years, I played a lot of sports including tennis, squash, running and general exercise. However, melanoma changed my life, and my health has considerably declined due to the rods and cement that now occupy my bones and legs.

## It all began with a shave

Whilst shaving my legs, I noticed that a very small freckle on my left shin had become raised. I saw two doctors at a medical centre, and both said it was fine, and proceeded to just freeze the area. I asked them were sure there was nothing sinister and they assured me that there was nothing to worry about. Unfortunately, a few days later, the area of the dot bubbled into a purple/black ghastly soft volcanic bulb and I knew I was in trouble. I went to a new medical practice and saw a third doctor. He immediately knew that it was a bad melanoma. Within two weeks, I saw a surgeon and from there my horrible melanoma journey took off.

117

We felt so sad and deflated by the news. My husband and girls all sat in a café near the doctor's surgery as I explained the situation. We all just cried and cried in disbelief. The hardest thing was that I was so advanced. There were not a lot of treatment options to stop it at that stage.

The doctors tried lots of drugs to stabilise the growth of the melanoma. I received a lot of chemotherapy that left me almost lifeless and in terrible pain. Every day I battled nausea and felt constantly sick and depressed. I cried a lot but had to be strong for my amazing family.

I was given Interferon as another round of treatment. My husband watched the nurses administer the drug and then went to put money in the parking meter. In the 10 minutes he was gone, I had such a bad reaction that I nearly died. Rob returned to find the doctors and nurses working on me. I felt as if all my organs were being squeezed tightly and I was in dreadful pain. It was scary times.

I was able to participate in a few clinical trials but found accessing them difficult.

I was the first guinea pig on the ipilimumab/nivolumab trial and never thought that it would be so emotionally moving, but it was. My husband had to ring around the world trying to get approval for me to have another shot at life. It really was my last and only chance to survive. I was given less than 12 months to live, and we were desperate. We got the go ahead thanks to my amazing husband Rob and my oncologist. Because of them, I am still here today to tell my story.

## Learning from experience

Hope is a strong and courageous word that I embraced throughout my journey. Without it, I can honestly say that I wouldn't be here. I have hope and faith always and every day. When confronted with any disease, some of us need something else to focus on and to help us simply get through. I turned towards having faith in God and hoped for the best. Cancer doesn't discriminate.

From this experience, I learned to take a deep breath and I prayed that I would get through the next step. I also placed faith in the doctors and nurses. They do their best to help and are still doing their best to help me be the best I can possibly be.

Although I wish we could have met under different circumstances, I met my 'brother' (Jay Allen) through this experience. I could not have asked for a nicer person to be by my side while I was in hospital. His compassion, belief, kindness, and love has helped get me through.

In the same way that Jay was there for me, I will always lend an ear to someone. Some people with a life-threatening illness such as melanoma may not want any help, but you can always ask, you can always listen, and you can always be there if they change their mind. Some are scared, but once they receive a hug or have their hand held, they really do open up. I will always be willing to help where I can, and I want to spread the word to be mindful of melanoma.

---

Being able to help others has been the biggest gift.

---

I am so lucky to see my family flourish and to have grandchildren come into my life. My husband Rob is an angel as he has such patience and love for me. Everyday he reminds me that he is blessed to have me. Despite melanoma, I am so lucky…

## Liz Davey – Ruth's daughter

At age 16, I am carer to my incredible mother, a survivor of stage 4 melanoma.

My relationship with Mum has evolved into the strongest of bonds. First as a daughter, then to carer, but most importantly the dearest of friends.

Melanoma. The word has become a constant in our lives. It turned our worlds upside down and spat us out the other end. I'll never forget the day we sat down as a family and Mum told my sisters and I about her diagnosis.

'But what do you mean Mum? This can't happen to you?'

Not to our mum. It's not fair. From that moment on, it felt as though our hearts were ripped straight out of us and torn to pieces.

We were confused, angry, and upset. Where to now?

Mum and I were living together while my father, Rob, was doing fly-in fly-out work and my sisters lived in Sydney. I was in Year 10 when Mum was diagnosed. Weekends involved driving down to the hospital in Sydney so that Mum could receive chemotherapy, and then nursing her while she was vomiting and in and out of a daze. I felt completely helpless. My mum, the warrior, was rapidly deteriorating right in front of my eyes.

Despite all of this she would always have a smile on her face and say, 'I'm okay darling, really, I just need to rest.' Little did I know that she was crippled with depression and fear. Mum became the master of putting on what most people would call 'a brave face'.

I would continuously research the internet and read articles and stories on how to fight cancer. I remember being in a constant state of confusion, not able to make any sense of the situation. In all honesty, it was a complete blur. My emotions felt numb, and I was in survival mode for Mum.

---

Be strong. Don't break down. Just do your best and stay positive!

---

Ruth and Jay

On one of our many visits to the hospital, Mum, Dad, and I were introduced to Jay Allen. From the moment we met him, he gave us a sense of comfort. This man is living proof that you CAN beat melanoma. Hope, we finally had some hope! Jay threw himself into Mum's survival battle and armoured up. 'We will fight this Ruth!' The key word being 'we'. Jay, a man with a heart of pure gold, living a life of service to others, diving in head-first to do whatever he could to help save Mum's life. Thank you, the powers that be! One can only hope to be this fortunate.

I have watched Mum and Jay's relationship flourish from two strangers sharing cancer journeys into a brotherly–sisterly bond. Mum no longer felt alone in the world of melanoma. She could open up to Jay about her concerns and he would open up about his experiences. Together they would make an unbreakable team.

Speaking on behalf of myself, my sisters, and my amazing father, we absolutely worship the ground Jay walks on. Without Jay's continuous encouragement, endless phone calls checking in with Mum and Dad, and his connections within the hospital, I can tell you with certainty that this journey would have been even tougher.

Life is full of emotional roller coasters. The highest of highs and lowest of lows. Thankfully, with people like Jay, these experiences in life can bring together some amazing people who become your lifeline. Don't be afraid to ask someone if they are okay. Be one of the Jays in the world – you are needed.

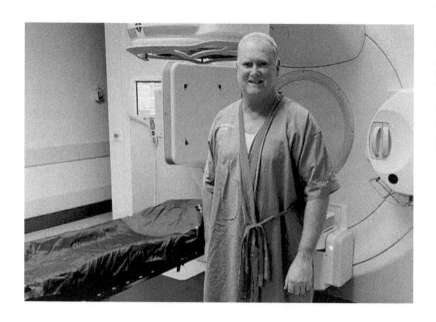

Anthony Simmons

# Anthony Simmons

The irony of my story is that my melanoma is not related to sun exposure.

I have a rare melanoma called acral lentiginous melanoma (ALM). When people see me limping and I mention that I have ALM, and show them the scars on my foot, they are surprised that the sun got to my heel. After I explain my story, they stand in amazement and simply say, 'I've never heard of it.' There is almost zero awareness. By sharing my story, I hope to be able to raise the profile of rare melanomas.

I was first diagnosed with melanoma at 49 years of age – a man in the prime of his life. I really did not know too much about this disease. I am not sure if it was arrogance or, like many people, I was just simply getting on with life and never gave it a thought that it could happen to me. I had intermittently applied sunscreen to my body on really hot days throughout my life but was never as diligent as we all should be.

## Background

I started my working life as an apprentice carpenter. In August 1988, I joined the army as a communications operator, operating radio and communication systems. I travelled to North Africa in 1993/94 as part of a United Nations contingent in the Western Sahara. I was discharged in 1996 to pursue my carpentry and building career. My military background served me well and followed me throughout my entire building career as I have been in leadership / management roles ever since. In 2001, the company I was working for was successful in its bid for the defence maintenance contract for New South Wales and I was asked to take on the senior project management role for the contract. Twenty years later I am still there.

I would like to think from a professional viewpoint that I am tough but fair. I have a very low tolerance for people who are not team players or who are, putting it simply, idiots. I love seeing people with a strong work ethic doing the hard work and advancing within the business or succeeding in new endeavours.

In life, the thing I love first and foremost is my beautiful family – my wife Donna and two daughters, Chantel and Bronte. I love spending time with my three girls and always wish we could spend more time together. We have a lot of good times and I love the challenge of living with three girls. It feels like I never left my childhood when I was surrounded by my three beautiful and supportive sisters, Maria, Lee and Suzie.

I have always loved a good time and a good laugh with family and friends: poker nights with the boys, family get togethers, golf, playing the guitar, football, cricket, tennis, fishing, the beach, the snow, long walks with my dog, and everything in between. I like to make sure that everyone in my life is happy and have what they need.

## The shattering diagnosis

A lot of pain in my right foot was the beginning of my eventual diagnosis. It got to the point where I could hardly walk. I ended up seeing a podiatrist who started treating me for plantar fasciitis. Treatment, or should I say 'mistreatment,' over the next 11 months did nothing to stop my increasing levels of pain. My wife suggested a second opinion. That was on a Monday and by the Friday of that first week in August 2018, I had undergone my first surgery, having been diagnosed with stage 3 acral lentiginous melanoma (ALM) – one of the rarest types of melanoma that is, in fact, unrelated to sun exposure.

Shattering! There is no other way to describe hearing the words, 'You have melanoma.' At that point, I did not really know much about it, and I remember going home with Donna and Googling 'melanoma' and 'moles on the soles of your feet'. ALM came up in the search results and the photos seemed so like the marks on my foot. I soon came to realise how serious it was, and from that moment on it became life changing.

I was then thrust into what I consider to be the hardest part of my melanoma journey. It was all so fast, and I had limited knowledge of melanoma and what to expect. All within a month of my diagnosis, I underwent three surgeries: biopsy surgery, then my right heel was degloved along with a sentinel node biopsy with lymph node removal behind my right knee and right groin. This was followed by a full foot reconstruction of the heel where the surgeons took a large skin and muscle graft from my left leg to rebuild my right foot. This surgery was performed by my excellent surgeon at a private hospital in Sydney, and I spent nine days afterwards on the ward. I went home for rehabilitation with nurse support to replace the dressings and check on my well-being. I was finally able to get mobile with the help of a knee scooter but was off work for nearly six months. I was homebound during this time and spent too much time alone feeling the effect of loneliness. I annoyed anyone I could at work and phoned friends, interrupting their day, but at least it helped to keep my mind off my own situation. The family dog and cat could only provide so much comfort during the day. ☺

I started 12 months of immunotherapy (nivolumab) as part of a clinical trial and received 26 fortnightly infusions at cancer centre. There were no real side effects apart from tiredness and fatigue, which I reported.

By November 2019, about 10 months into the trial, I developed stage 4 ALM. A metastasis was found in the upper lobe of my right lung. The upper lobe of my right lung was then resected to remove the metastasis along with nine lymph nodes on my chest wall.

One month later, a recurrence was detected in the primary site of the heel resulting in more surgery to remove the in-transit tumour and greater margin. Then, in May 2020, about 16 more in-transit tumours appeared on my right leg above the knee. Two of these were removed by my surgeon and biopsied to confirm that they were indeed melanoma tumours, but the rest are still there. Around the same time, a cluster of tumours in the middle of the lower lobe of my left lung showed up on CT scan. A punch biopsy was performed by sticking a biopsy needle through the back of my shoulder blade and into my lung. Fortunately, the pain from this was limited and only lasted a day or two, but it confirmed the presence of more melanoma. Ironically, this result gave me the ticket to start immunotherapy combination treatment.

In July 2020, I started ipilimumab/nivolumab treatment. I managed three out of the four planned treatments but ended up with a hepatitis infection in my liver which was diagnosed in November. This meant ceasing all further infusions including the planned further 12 months of nivolumab. The side effects of this treatment included fatigue, joint pain, rashes, and a general loss of mental and physical drive. My thyroid function was also destroyed, and I started lifelong thyroxine medication as a result. In February 2021, another lesion popped up against my pituitary gland which affected my testosterone and thyroid function.

In April 2021, I started to experience some lower back pain. A CT scan of the spine in late April revealed a spot measuring one centimetre in the lower sacral area (near S1). My oncologist insisted that we monitor it and scheduled an MRI which was booked for July 7 – the earliest the hospital could book me in. My GP insisted that we get on with a bone scan, and on June 24 it showed a three-centimetre tumour located on S1. I finally had the MRI on July 7, only a week ago at the time of writing, which confirmed that the tumour was now 5.5 cm x 4 cm and located to the left side of S1. It is impinging on my nerves to the left leg and is very painful to the point where it feels like my toes are on fire and very sore to touch. I have now been referred to a radiation oncologist in the hope that high dose stereotactic radiation therapy will relieve me of the severe nerve pain and shrink or remove the tumour so that I can get back to the status of 'stable disease'. As my lung surgeon said, 'Ah … melanoma – a life contract.' I certainly know what he means.

## Facebook to friendship

When I was in hospital recovering from the ten-hour foot re-construction, my wife Donna was sitting in my room and mentioned some good Facebook support groups for melanoma. I was still heavily medicated at the time and simply said that I would look at them later.

The next day I was scrolling through my Facebook feed and decided to search for melanoma. There was a group that had a feed from the City to Surf and there was this guy Jay Allen, 'The Melanoma Man,' standing next to my GP. They were warming up to run 14 kilometres and to raise money for an institute. I was so excited to see my GP there with this Jay guy. What a bloody champion I thought! 😊

Anthony Simmons, Jay Allen and members of ASCF

I searched Facebook for 'The Melanoma Man' and joined the page. A few days later, I decided to call Jay directly as his number was on the page. I told Jay my story over the phone. I mentioned that I had always been keen on raising money for cancer foundations and asked if I could help. Jay was so pumped and his energy over the phone was so infectious. He told me that he does a lot of walks from his work (at that time) into Circular Quay, or over to Barangaroo, via the Sydney Harbour Bridge, and asked if I would like to meet up with him for a walk. I laughed and reminded Jay that I was in hospital and recovering from a total foot reconstruction. We laughed, and I said that I would take him up on the opportunity for a walk once I recovered.

About four months into my recovery, I finally got to take Jay up on his offer. We went for that walk across the bridge, and since that walk Jay has been there for me and many others.

In between my nivolumab trial in 2019, I ended up joining Jay and his support crew for 12 days of one of Jay's walks. I have always been a good advocate for raising money for a good cause. My efforts have mostly been for different cancer foundations, but I never thought I would be a cancer patient myself one day. I raised a massive total of $20,020 together with my sister Lee who organised a special band night at the Broulee Surf Club. I left Jay in Canberra, shot off to Sydney for my next round of nivolumab, and raced back down to Batemans Bay to catch up with the team again. We held a surf club function and raised around $10,000.

Having Jay as a friend and source of infectious strength has helped me through the toughest times. During my lung surgery, Jay was there and visited me in hospital. Even now, as he recovers from his latest bout of cancer, he has called in to see how I am and to wish me all the best for the appointment with my radiation oncologist. We have a great time together and share a lot of laughs. We playfully call each other 'brother' or 'champion' all the time, but to me Jay is a brother and a true champion. If ever I need to put a team together again, Jay would be my first pick.

## Lessons learnt

### Lesson 1:
### *Surround yourself with great care providers*

I have learnt through this experience that there are a lot of very clever people in the world who can provide great medical care and assistance. You can gain a lot of comfort and assurance from having a great care team. My GP and the original surgeon who reconstructed my right foot are only ever a phone call away and, if something is not right, they are onto it immediately. As I come up to my three year 'cancerversary', I have been blessed with a great care team who remain on my side.

### Lesson 2:
### *The footprint you leave on Earth*

If you are to suddenly leave this world, what are you leaving behind? In my case, I will be leaving three beautiful girls. I have made sure that they will be comfortable when I am gone. I am fortunate in that I have a good super fund and a good life insurance package through work. If I go tomorrow, I take comfort in knowing that they know how much I love them understand how much happiness they have brought into my life. Not everyone gets to have this in place before they go. On a funny note, I am cognisant of the fact that I have a lot of stuff! There are tools and knick knacks that I have held onto for way too long. Every week, I make it a priority to throw out the rubbish, or give it away, so that my girls do not have to deal with it when I am gone. 😊

## Lesson 3:
### Pick your team

Make sure you have a good team around you. Reach out to relevant support groups and services, and other respectable groups on social media. Take in all the positive stories you read and try to find relevance to your own story.

## Lesson 4:
### Mind and body fitness

Always be on the front foot and keep on top of your mind and body fitness. Cry if you must and never be afraid to let it all out. Learn about your situation and search for the positives. In times of darkness, think of things to get you out of those moments. Talk to friends, walk the dog, do something you like to take your mind off the cancer and take you to a happy place. Let the people in your life know that you love them. Fight and fight!

## Lesson 5:
### Making arrangements brings comfort

Once you have been diagnosed with melanoma and understand that it can be life-limiting, there will be events as life continues that will trigger emotional thoughts. Last year, in August 2020, one of my nieces was getting married. The reception was held at a beautiful reception house called Jaspers just outside Berry in NSW. Berry had received 300 millimetres of rain that weekend and we were just coming out of the first Covid lockdown, which had not made life any easier. The service was supposed to be held outside in the gardens, but it was moved inside due to the rain. As my brother-in-law, Peter, and his beautiful daughter were about to walk in, they paused in the doorway giving me a clear view of Peter, the bride, and my two amazingly beautiful daughters. It could not have been framed any better. The vision was beautiful but provoked the sudden thought: 'Shit! I may never get to do this with my two girls.' I welled up like you would not believe …

A couple of months afterwards, I asked my sister Lee, who is married to Peter, if she would ask Peter to join Donna's brother, Jason, and do the honour on my behalf of walking Chantel and Bronte down the aisle in case I am unable to do so. I intend to fight like hell to still be here for that honour, but at least I have planted the seed and made the arrangement if I am not. While these kinds of thoughts are hard to grapple with, there is comfort in knowing that you are putting things in place.

## Final reflections

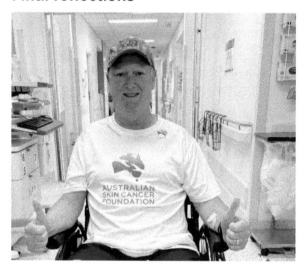

Anthony Simmons

In the past five years, my family has been through just too much cancer. My mother has had a very large ovarian tumour removed, undergone chemotherapy and radiation therapy, and is still surviving at the age of 79. My father, Terry, has battled both bladder and bowel cancer and will celebrate his 80th birthday in October 2021.

I have always had a feeling of being bullet proof in life and have tried to keep a positive attitude since the diagnosis. There have been some days which are very hard, and you think that you are not going to win the battle. I know being diagnosed has affected my eldest daughter Chantel deeply, and it still does. My younger daughter, Bronte, handles it differently but no doubt as strongly. She always sees me as 'Superman' and my number in her phone contacts is listed as 'Superman' – God bless her!

The past three years has brought us a lot closer as a family and I love the strength, love, and support they all give me. My hope is to keep fighting every recurrence to buy the time I need to find a cure for this horrible disease. At the same time, I have learnt to accept the worst-case scenario and that I may not beat this insidious disease.

If I am ever told that there are no further options, and we could be talking about months, I will grab that number and double it. And once I double it, I will triple it. I will fight for them for as long as it takes.

*Anthony 'Simmo' Simmons sadly passed away to melanoma on 13th September 2022*

Emma Page with Sofia, Jack and Harry

# Emma Page

I'm telling my story because melanoma doesn't discriminate. I chose that there is no other option but to live and that no-one would raise my children but me.

I was raised in Dural, outside of Sydney, and now live in Piggabeen in far north New South Wales with my family – children Sofia aged 16, Jack 13, Harry 5, and my partner in crime, Graham. We live on five acres and have three horses, three dogs and two cows. To say I love animals is an understatement – they are all my babies! Riding my horses soothes the soul. We are a tight family and I am from a tight family. I am one of four and I love my two sisters and brother. We are goal setters and always striving to better ourselves. We are also competitive, and that mindset has proven valuable…

Before settling in Piggabeen, I lived in England for 12 years running a hotel on Park Lane and my two eldest were born there. I would throw them in the car and get on the ferry to France for a weekend or jump on a plane and go to Italy – anywhere that we needed to explore. I would rather create experiences and memories with the children than buy toys – the poor kids had one box of toys! They don't remember the toys, but they do remember the trips! Our most recent family holiday was a week sailing around the Whitsundays. We went to random places along the way, truly living life, enjoying our surroundings, and taking the mickey out of each other.

We run a family business GJM Electrical and Air Conditioning. I take care of the office and administration, and Graham works his magic. However, my most important job is keeping my family in check. Every day is a hustle. I exercise and love it so am up at 4.30am to make it to boxing at 5am or a run. I weight train, run, walk, and do the very occasional yoga, which I don't really like. I love the outdoors and being pushed to my limits. I also love entertaining, so we constantly have friends and neighbours over and there is always food and drinks on the table. Then there's the kids' drama classes after school in Byron Bay, piano on Tuesdays, army cadets on Wednesday, and rugby or Thursday and Friday. On Saturdays, I drive my daughter to and from work and any other activity the kids have, and finally Sunday is the day of rest. No-one is allowed to book anything on a Sunday without checking in with mum the Uber driver. Apparently, I need to slow down!

## The nightmare begins

I was diagnosed with melanoma at the age of 37. At the time of my diagnosis, I was very fit and very in touch with my body. I had noticed a lump under my armpit after a boxing class and thought that it was just a swollen gland. I didn't feel unwell. I was tired and didn't have much of an appetite, but that was typical given our busy family life.

The following week, I went with Graham to the doctor to sort out his insulin as he is a type 1 diabetic. As we were about to leave, and after teaching the doctor how to squat properly in her office, I said, 'Doctor, I have a lump under my arm.' She had a look and said that it was probably an ingrown hair and to stop shaving! I replied, 'I would rather be dead than be hairy!' Her response was to send me for an ultrasound which revealed a tumour under my arm that needed to be removed.

## Dealing with diagnosis

The tumour was melanoma, which was bad enough, but the staging after surgery revealed the next bomb – it was in my lymph nodes and stage IIIC.

We were in complete and utter shock! How could the fittest, most healthy member of our family have stage IIIC melanoma with no evidence of the primary cancer? With this diagnosis, however, came some sense of personal relief that it was me and not my children. I knew I was the strongest and that I could handle anything!

Graham went into research mode. Knowledge is power, so that is what he focused on – saving me! As far as the children were concerned, I downplayed it a lot! It was just a cold, right?! My family and friends were devastated, felt helpless, but then went into action!

There was nothing that they did not do. Especially 'my girls,' my besties from school. They were my superheroes and went above and beyond.

Despite my fierce determination and positivity, one of the hardest things was suddenly being out of control. Our lives were turned upside down without any warning. We had to learn very quickly everything we possibly could about statistics, treatments, Western medicine, alternative medicine, and its effects.

I also did not want sympathy nor to be 'that cancer patient.' As an example, access to the vein in my right arm was impossible and my left vein was being hammered. It took me months to come to terms with the fact that I needed a port, which would have reduced all that extra time I sat in the oncology chair while they tried to access a vein. Once it was in, I wished I had done it sooner. You could say that I was in 'healthy denial.' I just segmented each stage, ticked it off the list, prepared for the next, and found the fight I needed to move closer towards becoming cancer-free.

## Surgery and treatment

I had a full right axillary dissection to remove the tumour and almost lost my main vein. Thankfully, it was able to be saved and repaired.

After surgery, I suffered from a week of chronic pain that could not be controlled with medication. I was taken back to the operating table, spent another week in hospital in the same position, ended up with bed sores, and learned that my nerve had been sutured during the first surgery. I then proceeded to have nivolumab for just over a year.

We handled it like pros. The children would come to treatment and the ongoing infusions became another family day in oncology. The nurses looked after them as much as they did me. We laughed a lot blowing up gloves, and my daughter would often play with my mechanical chair, sending me up high or backwards. We spoke to other patients, listened to tunes with the staff, and just made the best we could out of a very bad situation.

My body responded well to nivolumab in the clinical sense. I had a very small black spot show on my lung on one of my PET scans, but after four months it was gone. We therefore knew the treatment was

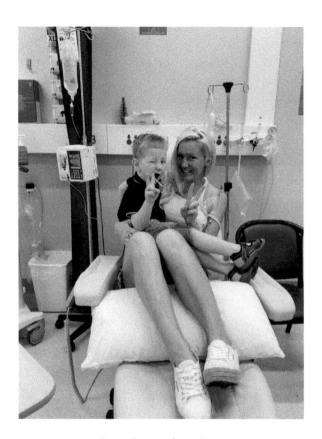

Emma Page and son Harry

working. No matter how strong my mind was though, it didn't stop the side effects of treatment which I just had to manage. My throat and neck felt swollen, and about an hour after treatment I would start to feel nauseous, making it very difficult to eat. I would have some cannabidiol (CBD) oil which would calm the nausea and enable me to eat, if only a little. I needed to keep my energy up as I had a family to run. I had a lot of fluid retention and still do most days. The fatigue was the worst part of it all. My body wanted to rest but my mind was telling me otherwise.

Today, I suffer from lymphoedema in my right arm, breast and upper back due to the surgery and lymph node removal. The lymphoedema does get me down some days but I have tricks, know how my body works, and what I need to do to make sure I can remove the fluid myself.

I also have hypothyroidism due to the immunotherapy and need to take thyroxin daily. This was very difficult to manage in the beginning. My bloods were so erratic, my thyroid levels were up and down, and it took months to work out why I was so fatigued. Getting the dose of thyroxin correct took months. It took a year of trial and error before I started to slowly regain energy. Being an energetic person and mentally REALLY having to push myself daily to be the best version of myself, and to get things done, was one of the hardest things to deal with.

## The Melanoma Man

I came to know Jay Allen initially via Instagram. He had seen that I was undergoing treatment and sent me a message. He explained he was a 12-year stage 3 melanoma survivor and asked if I was doing OK. Messages went back and forth, and I realised that I was not alone. Once you open up about your situation, it i surprising to learn just how many people out there are affected and how much support is available. It was so comforting to have someone understand exactly what I was going through who was giving strength, hope and positive messages.

I can sum Jay up in one word: Legend. He is selfless, determined and very like-minded. I think that is why we have such mutual respect. He has a beautiful wife and children and there is nothing he would not do to be around for his family. The awareness one man has brought to the nation and beyond is remarkable even whilst suffering himself. Jay is really the vital link connecting all melanoma sufferers.

## Reflections

### Hope

Many people seem to have hope when it comes to a serious diagnosis. I did not hope for anything – EVER! From day one, I was on a mission to get to the next stage and to get the old 'Pagie' back. I didn't want this to consume our lives and I treated it like a cold. Like I said to my children, 'I do what I have to do, take the medicine, and we move on with our lives.' There were many tough days, but I knew where I had to be and kept pushing forward.

I certainly didn't want my children to hear the word 'cancer' and fear it. So, I treated it like a cold and tried to show no weakness when they were around.

### Smell the roses

The experience has also taught me the true meaning of 'life is short'. I have made a conscious note to continue to live my life without regrets. I have always lived life to the fullest but now I stop to take a breath. As my very first boss said to me, 'Pagie, stop and smell the roses.'

### Positive mindset

Maintaining a positive mindset is everything even through the darkest of days. You can change a great deal with a positive mind and attitude. I would always try and go to treatment well-presented no matter how bad I felt. Graham and I would always go for a lunch date or a juice straight after treatment. Even if it was hard to stomach food, I still did it and it was something to look forward to. I would then go home and be poorly, have a sleep, wake up and make sure I was OK by the time the children were brought home from school. The mind is a powerful thing, and you can do it!

### Be good to your body

Like a car, you do not put diesel into a petrol engine. Put good things in even during treatment. Keep your diet clean, juice and juice some more, and try to maintain physical activity. Give yourself the chance to have the best possible outcome.

## Fit, strong and sharing

Today I am fit, strong, healthy, and doing better than ever. I did, unfortunately, suffer with another issue. I required a procedure for cervical cancer apparently because I am immune compromised. The virus often responsible for cervical cancer had a party whilst I was poorly, but I am pleased to say that the doctors got all the margins, and I am back in the clear. So, it's time to get even fitter to support Jay with his next epic fundraising walk!

During this entire experience, my animals were my therapy while I was unwell. I know how animals can help heal in ways we don't even realise and knew I had to share this with others. I have now created a special place called '10 Winchester Farm'. Winchester Farm is where people with disabilities can find connection and improve self-esteem and social skills through animals. We now have four horses, two dogs, two cows and many ducks and birds. Our latest addition is Macy, a 28-inch miniature horse who is a darling. The changes and connections I see daily are heart-warming. I am blessed to be a part of people's journeys.

---

https://www.instagram.com/10_winchester_farm

---

Jason Wells, with Kara, Lucy, Lexi and Luna.

# Jason Wells

I am sharing my story for two reasons: To raise awareness about melanoma and hopefully encourage others to be more cautious with their sun protection. And to help or comfort others. When I was first diagnosed, I initially felt alone in my situation, and I had so many questions. After finding melanoma support communities, I found a sense of ease and comfort in hearing other people's stories and built new friendships and connections.

I'm a renderer by trade and live on the outskirts of Melbourne, Victoria. However, following my melanoma diagnosis I switched to plastic injection moulding where I have more flexible hours that are more suited to my lifestyle.

My wife is Kara, and we have three children – Lucy aged 6, Lexi 4 and Luna just 3 months at the time of writing. I was diagnosed with metastatic melanoma on December 19, 2017, at the age of 46. At that time, we had two children under the age of two, and we missed out on building those special moments while I was undergoing treatment. Going on little family holidays, when and where we can (thanks coronavirus!), are now extra special as we make up for lost time.

I love motorbikes, restored cars, working out in the gym, getting outside with my girls, and staying as active as I can. I also love socialising with friends and family, meeting new people, making new friends wherever I go, and a good chat! Anyone who meets me would be lucky to get away in under 20 minutes!

Today, I am cancer free! My main hope is to remain healthy, to enjoy every second of life and to appreciate the little things. Time is passing so quickly. I am just thankful and continuously hopeful that I remain well so I can continue to watch my children grow.

## A devastating lump

I felt a lump under my left armpit as I leant over Lexi's cot while putting her to sleep one evening. I went to the doctor and was diagnosed with pneumonia as it was assumed that the lymph node was just severely inflamed. However, three weeks later the lump had still not disappeared and had increased in size. The doctor reviewed it again and this time took blood tests and sent a core biopsy of the lump off to pathology. After an agonising two weeks wait, the results came back that the lump was a malignant mass. I was given a referral to a cancer treatment centre and was admitted within the week.

I had my first PET scan but only from the neck down. The PET scan did not reveal any primary tumour sites or any other indication of cancer, and so the doctors sent me off for an MRI of my head. It discovered four separate tumours in my brain, one of which was haemorrhaging. I was classified as having stage 4 metastatic melanoma with axillary and brain involvement. In total, five tumour sites were identified at the time.

---

I was told that without treatment my life expectancy was between 18 months to a maximum of two years. Even with a treatment plan, there was no guarantee that I would live longer.

---

How the diagnosis affected myself and my family at the beginning of my cancer journey can be summed up in five words:

1. Shocked.
   I led what most (including myself) would consider a healthy and active lifestyle. I had never smoked. For the first few moments, I couldn't believe it and was left wondering how.

2. Devastated
   Kara and I were planning our wedding. Our two girls were under two and we were planning our third child. After my initial reaction, all I could think about was what I would miss: the girls growing up and all their milestones, a life alongside Kara, and the little daily things that I thought I'd never get to see or do again.

3. Concerned
   How would my wife and children manage? We have such a supportive

142

network of friends and family so I wasn't concerned that they would ever be completely alone, but after a few months, how would they cope?

4. Anxious
The constant anxiety and fear were consuming, and every day there was a new stressor. Even just a regular cold would have me playing mind games and wondering, 'Could this be the cancer?' Before every check-up, appointment, scan, and treatment the anxiety just intensified.

5. Terrified
I am the man of the house, but throughout this I felt helpless and scared. At times I was terrified. Cancer is still so unknown, and no one could give us answers because no one knows! This was a hard hurdle to overcome, facing a disease that even with today's technology and scientific advances did not offer a cure.

## Treatment

I was immediately started on steroids until later results found that I have the BRAF V600E mutation and radiation was deemed necessary. The dose regime was whole brain radiation, over a five-day period. As this was discovered during the Christmas period, I ended up having three days of treatment in a row, a three-day break, and then the final two days. Each treatment delivered a harsh 20 Gy dose of radiation.

I was then started on dabrafenib plus trametinib. Eight months after my original diagnosis, a sixth tumour was found in my right arm. The doctors decided it was best to switch to a combination approach involving radiation plus the immunotherapy drugs ipilimumab and nivolumab.

The side effects from the treatment medications were inconsistent and pushed me around. One day I would feel normal, able to play with the girls, go to work and feel fine. The next I'd be bedridden and unable to help Kara with the girls, or even go to work. Sometimes the effects were so bad that they would hit me for six for an entire week. However, after a third dose of immunotherapy in December 2018, the doctors told me that all my tumours had disappeared! Around this time, I had to switch medications due to being diagnosed with hydrophysitis. This was a serious and late onset side effect due to the medications. My pituitary gland had stopped functioning and, as a result, I was gaining weight and visibly puffy all over my body. I was immediately hospitalised, and my medication regimen was changed in an attempt to resolve these side effects.

I began prednisolone – a single-agent immunotherapy drug that would eventually be dose reduced. I then switched over to a lesser drug and was on this for two years. After being on constant medications for four years since late 2017, I've now been off all major medicines for a total of nine months! I continue to take hydrocortisone 20mg and Coversyl® 5mg tablets daily and will continue to do so for the rest of my life. It feels good to be free in a sense, but I remain scared of the unknown and what could happen. I recently spoke with my doctors who informed me that I would be eligible for some clinical trials in the event of a recurrence.

My scans have remained clear since June 7, 2020.

## Finding support

My wife Kara did a lot of research online about how to deal with the situation with young kids. She found many online groups and pages offering support. One such page was 'The Melanoma Man.' The ability to read what others were going through and the number of uplifting stories helped more than words can say. Additionally, Jay was there for me, like he is for countless others affected by this disease. Whether it was a call or message, Jay was never too far away, and he was a true friend during the hardest of times.

We participated in one of Jay's walks in May of 2019. The walk itself was to raise money for clinical trials and melanoma research, but it also provided a support group for those who were present and affected in some way. It gave me hope to inspire and encourage more work to be done for future cancer patients. It also helped to keep the memories of those we have lost alive.

We were very fortunate to feel extremely supported by the

hospital, our friends and family, and my workplace. The doctors and nurses were wonderful, not only to me, but also to my wife Kara throughout the four immensely challenging years. My boss and my colleagues were there in more ways than one to help my family and I make it through those rough and manic weeks. I can never repay them. People literally came together for us – family, friends I'd known for decades, and new friends, including some met through this unwanted experience. They took me to appointments, prepared and delivered meals for us all and, when times were particularly tough, kept up the general maintenance and the organisation of even the simplest of things. The overall generosity of everyone in my life filled me with such gratitude and love. I will carry their love and they will have my appreciation forever.

## Hope

The hardest part of my diagnosis was dealing with the:

1. Uncertainty

Will it ever come back? When will it come back?

2. Fear

What does it mean for my family, for Kara and the girls? What happens if I beat it this time only to have it return?

3. Waves

From the moment of diagnosis, it has felt like being on one wild rollercoaster ride. One day I would feel angry and sad or be sick and under the weather. The next, I was happy and feeling great, almost as though it had never happened, and then I would feel grateful. It has certainly made me appreciate every single moment I get to spend with my family and friends.

Hope also came in waves. At the start, when I was first told I had stage 4 melanoma, I was at my lowest point with little to no hope. Then, when I went home and saw my wife and our two little girls, I knew I had to keep on going. Each day, I had to hope for a future with them rather than thinking of all the memories I'd miss out on if I was not around. Today in 2021, with the arrival of our third little girl just a few months ago, I am looking at the positives over any negatives, and I try my best to live each day to the fullest. I honestly no longer think about melanoma daily and it's not who I am or what defines me or my family. I often find that I forget my cancer diagnosis and just look forward. I am becoming more and more hopeful.

---

Don't take life for granted. Appreciate what you have while you can.

---

## Reflections

Having this opportunity to tell my story and to share it on such a large platform is unbelievable. One day, my children will be able to read this and understand what happened from perhaps a different perspective. Being able to read people's stories is priceless, as is listening to and meeting others who have walked down the same path. Without Jay, this never would have been possible for me. It is something that I can never repay but I remain always grateful.

To anyone diagnosed with melanoma, my advice would be to eat well, fight and don't give up! Some days are harder than others but mentally I found it was best to not let it control my life. Even though at times you may feel that you are alone, understand that you are not. There is a huge community online that you and your family can lean on and reach out to.

And finally, to anyone reading this, please remember that sunscreen and sun protection is important! Melanoma can happen to anyone.

Julie Randall

# Julie Randall

I hope for a world that has a cure for all melanomas and cancers. The devastating destruction it causes to all aspects of life for patients and their families is insurmountable. The level of resilience it takes to overcome this disease and move on and find some sort of cryptic meaning is enormous. I am one of the lucky ones who has now found my life's purpose.

These days, I spend my time working, mentoring patients, loving my husband and family, and studying and teaching the power of the mind. I am the author of my best-selling memoire, *Patient 71*, a dedication to my melanoma journey which I wrote in the hope that it inspires other patients and loved ones around the world. I also speak about my experience so that people who find themselves in the unenviable situation of a melanoma diagnosis can feel that they are not alone. I love speaking even though Covid has, at least for now, put the brakes on the speaker's circuit.

*Patient 71* by Julie Randall
Available from: amazon.com.au,
booktopia.com.au or julierandall.com.au

## The death sentence I vowed to fix

In 2014, four days after my 50th birthday celebrations, as I drove to work in Sydney's CBD, I was practising gratitude and thanked the universe for my family, my husband, the sun, and the blue sky. I was feeling so lucky to be me and felt as fit as a fiddle as I was training for an over 45's state level touch football tournament.

At 1pm, I was taken out to lunch by one of the directors and a work colleague. After lunch, I came back to the office and sat down at my desk. My boss asked me a question and I could not answer him. Something was wrong and, in that split second, I knew that I was in big trouble. An ambulance was called, and I was taken to emergency. Within 24 hours I was told I had stage 4 advanced cancer with tumours in my brain, both lungs, liver, pancreas, and lymph nodes. In that moment came devastation, upheaval and despair as the life-crushing and dream-killing reality of the situation set in. In the blink of an eye, I went from as fit as a fiddle to having an automatic death sentence.

My teenage daughters were distraught. I was more worried about the carnage I would leave behind than death itself, which I was told was about nine months away at best. I made a promise to my children that I would 'fix it' and that I would not die.

---

At that time, I could not find one single person who had survived a similar diagnosis.

---

I had the tumour in my brain removed. It was terrifying and you would not wish the pain on your worst enemy. I started chemotherapy. It was not a cure for melanoma, but the only real tool left in the shed. It was a toxic time-buyer with a response rate of only 10%, but I needed to buy time to research other options and search for a cure. I tolerated the chemotherapy quite well, but lost my hair and had significant weight loss as I also gave up sugar and overhauled my diet. The psychological effect of seeing me in that condition for my teenage daughters, husband, family, and friends was undeniable. It was heart-wrenching for me to have to put them through that, but it needed to be done.

## Research for a cure

I had to find the strength to tell myself there had to be a first person to survive this even though my mind monsters would tell me, 'You will die from this.' I had promised my daughters I would 'fix it,' and I had to believe and have hope that somehow I would maintain that promise. And so, the research began.

I found a clinical trial in Portland, Oregon, USA. They were trialling what was then a new immunotherapy treatment that was having promising responses. There was no long-term data, but the results were encouraging. The trouble was that the trial was only available for US citizens and was closed to recruitment given that they had reached the target of 70 patients. I begged and pleaded for three-and-a-half months for the hospital to give me a place in the trial. My husband followed-up. I wouldn't take no for an answer, and finally I received the phone call that literally changed my life. I became Patient 71.

The hardest part was leaving my family, friends, and my beautiful golden retriever Roxy behind and not knowing if I would ever come home. It was sooooo difficult, but I had to suffer severe short-term pain in the hope of some long-term gain. I was homesick and in a strange place, but I tolerated the drug well. The people at the hospital were lovely and amazing and looked after me. I took on fundraising activities for them and helped to raise over $750,000.

---

It worked! I am still here and cancer free nine years later.

---

## The power of the promise

For someone who is well, it is worth remembering that life as you know it can be taken away in an instant. Living for the day is essential. Joy and laughter are our birth right and should be scheduled into daily routines as a must do. It is important to find your passion and live with your own purpose. As humans, we very often don't live up to our full potential. In fact, we are stronger and have more courage than we think we have, and there is true power in a promise.

If you have recently been diagnosed, it is difficult to find a single message to fit all as everyone is in different stages of the disease. My advice to anyone diagnosed with melanoma or another cancer is as follows:

1. After the initial shock, allow yourself some grieving time.
2. Decide that you will find the courage and the strength to get though. We are braver and stronger than we think we are!
3. Never give up on hope. There is no such thing as false hope. Hope is hope!
4. Remember that research is ongoing – more treatments are on the horizon.
5. Where possible, look after yourself. Body, mind, and spirit. This also means finding the right support network. Friends, family, a counsellor, or someone like Jay Allen (my hero!).
6. Try to make peace with your situation as it stands in the present, and perhaps create a vision board for the future.
7. Do not fight with your body but encourage it in every way possible to respond to treatment.
8. Love yourself like your life depends on it.
9. As hard as it may seem at first, re-focus and turn your attention to something joyful. Start something new or do things that bring some sense of joy. There is data showing the power of positivity and joy in the face of disease.
10. Do not let melanoma or cancer take any more of your life than it must.

---

We are not cancer or melanoma. We are still the essence of us.

---

Watch Julie's story on 60 Minutes (2017):
https://www.youtube.com/watch?v=sHS-3p9g_Os

Marisa Worling

# Marisa Worling

I'm sharing my story to spread awareness and hope, as I know when I was diagnosed I was looking for stories of survival to give me hope.

I love being outdoors and being active. I love my family, my husband and our two boys and their partners. All my family (Mum, Dad, and sisters and their families) live close by for which I'm very grateful.

I'm an accountant and have been in this profession since 1995.

We all love to go camping, I love trail running and have started to learn to play golf. We have a spoodle called Tillie – she is 7 years old.

## How it began

It all started when I was competing in Ultra Trail Australia in the Blue Mountains in 2017, I was in the 50km event. Leading up to the event I had a sore ankle and just put it down to overuse injury. Right from the start of the race it hurt but I thought it could warm up and be okay, I stopped at 3km in tears that I wasn't sure if I could go on, but I don't like quitting so I pushed on.

At one of the aide stations I met a family that were all doing the event together – two sisters and their dad and another couple of friends. I asked if I could tag along with them as they were going to be walking. I spent a good part of the day with them and it was good to chat and take my mind off the pain. But about 5pm it was getting late and I had dropped back from the group and we came into the aide station at the 28km mark, I asked the medic what they thought of my leg and they couldn't really say what was wrong and if I should stop. I decided to pull out, I still remember sitting on the park bench devastated and feeling that I had let myself down and my family and my trainer.

My primary melanoma was never found.

I was diagnosed after a period of tests.

After we got back home I had an x-ray which didn't show anything; so I pushed to get an MRI as I knew something wasn't right.

155

The MRI showed the tumour in my Left Tibia. It took a couple more weeks till the doctors decided to do a Petscan and then not only could they see the tumour in my Tibia but also a tumour in my skull.

From these results it all moved pretty quick, I met my oncologist, then a neurosurgeon, had a bone marrow biopsy, as at this stage they didn't know what type of cancer I had. The neurosurgeon said I had to have a craniotomy performed in the next couple of days. It was a couple of days after the craniotomy that the oncologist came and saw me with the results. I was devastated and couldn't believe when he told me it was melanoma.

I was devastated. I'm not sure what words I would use to describe how my family felt. Our boys were only in their early teens. We all stayed strong together and kept being hopeful and took it all one day at a time.

The hardest part of the diagnosis was not knowing what the future held for me or my family. I didn't want to leave them.

## Treatment

I had a craniotomy, then surgery to insert a nail in the left tibia. I then commenced radiation on my leg and skull and also had immunotherapy, Yervoy (ipilimumab).

I lost my hair on my head from the radiation, except a little bit of fringe and the back remained so I could wear a hat and no one would have to know. It took a bit to look in the mirror and accept what I looked like.

I got a rash which was a bit uncomfortable.

But through this experience I learnt that I could be strong and focused.

After I got over the shock and spoke to different specialists I had hope and focussed on what I could do to help my body recover. My advice for anyone who is diagnosed with melanoma or even another type of cancer, would be to stay positive, there are treatments available and these are advancing all the time. There are options, please don't give up. It's important to get a skin check, but it is also important to listen to your body and if you feel something isn't right. Push the doctors to get the tests till you are happy that everything is okay.

Because if I hadn't have pushed to get the MRI I'm not sure what would have happened.

Jay means a lot, his strength to not only deal with his health but the support he provides to the Melanoma community is amazing. His passion to spread awareness and provide skin checks to everyone is inspiring.

Philip Murray

# Philip Murray

38Yrs. First diagnosed Stage III, 23 Dec 2005, after six months of an experienced GP stating it wasn't cancer.

56Yrs. Second diagnosis Stage III, June 2023, after a mole started getting itchy and not healing over when rubbed.

I'm sharing my story to give hope that a diagnosis is not a bad thing, you at least know what you're dealing with. From my first diagnosis to the second, some 18 years apart, there have been astronomical leaps in research and treatment. Drug treatments, knowledge and care support weren't that great in the past, but nowadays things are so much better with organisations like ASCF.

I love spending time with my family and close friends. I'm so thankful to be married 34 years to an amazing woman, and have two sons in their twenties, the eldest is recently married. I enjoy fishing, working with horses, my gardens, and watching sport.

Described in one of my job roles as 'energetic and passionate', this sums up why I love working in roles that keep my brain and body active. I've worked in roles from horticulture, mental health to emergency service rescue and management, eventually working for myself in training and assessing for 15 years.

My number one holiday location is Fiji with the family, we feel so relaxed when we're there. I also loved Bora Bora for our 20th wedding anniversary, which was a surprise for my wife. It was also a celebration three year's post cancer. Both locations are awesome for their beauty and calmness. I also love the Australian bush, it's so unique!

I enjoy my collections of stamps, coins, chainsaw memorabilia… Before my mum passed away a couple of years ago, she started giving away things to the family that she knew or thought they might like. Actually, she was doing it for twenty plus years, so a lesson I learnt from her is that our things are just things! Maybe my things are just junk?

I'm not a fan of laziness and buck passers. And I don't do dumb people, you know the ones who ask you something with a $1000 phone in their hands – I give them the look my mother used to do, over my glasses. I'm pretty laid back and casual otherwise.

The first time I was diagnosed with melanoma I felt, in a nutshell, shock, anger and disbelief.

I had a lump around the size of 10c piece in the upper thigh/groin region. There was no primary site ever located. It was finally taken out with a hernia operation when I asked the surgeon to do it at the same time. This was six months after I first noticed it. Follow-up surgery was intense and 24 more nodes (5 showing more melanoma) and 104 staples later, I was happy it was gone. The drain stayed in for 6 weeks and I went on to this new drug trial. It was early immunotherapy and was run out of Germany through Melbourne. Treatment was through Melanoma Institute Australia which was based at RPA in Sydney. I thought, *well I can be a guinea pig, sign me up*. Anything to avoid chemo or radio therapy.

What did I learn from that experience? To trust your instincts and take charge of your own health. Don't just rely on medical staff to tell you what you should do; do your own research and make sound informed decisions.

With the second diagnosis I thought, *oh great this is surely not happening now; the past three years have been nothing but crap*. Quickly followed by, *hang on, I'm experienced in this, what's my plan and who do I need on my team going forward?* My wife insisted I get a mole checked in late March. We'd had a spa installed in the February and it just happened to have jets at the same level as the mole on the shoulder blade. We believe the spa may have been a saving grace, in that it showed the mole wasn't happy with being wet or bumped. The histology came back as it being 7.8 mm deep and clark scale IV. Please don't look at statistics, remember you're in charge of your health outcomes by selecting the appropriate treatment. Also remember that everybody's story is different. My story is not your story.

We contacted my mate Jay, The Melanoma Man, whom we had

known since forming the first support group for survivors and families in NSW back in 2008. Knowing his experience and contacts really helped alleviate some of the fears that re-emerged from the past.

So, second surgery with wider excision and sentinel nodes removed from the neck and armpit showed two more nodes with melanoma.

My wife and I had already agreed on a plan, get it all cut out and forget statistics. Get a referral to the top oncologist around and if available get on a drug trial. Well, it so happened I got it all. Why? Because I asked for it and did my research.

Firstly, don't ever just do this on your own. If possible, don't put up walls to protect loved ones. It doesn't work and it helps no one.

The hardest part from my point of view is fear and guilt. The first time I thought, *I have a wife and young kids, how are they going to cope if I die?* I'm not going to be around to see them grow up. Would my wife remarry, and would she be loved like I love her? With my second diagnosis my kids are grown up, what must they all be feeling? How will my wife and I involve them along with my extended family? In the end it was easy because I decided to be open and honest and there would be 'no walls'.

I've found that works for me, however being raw or real with others when this thing called cancer gets thrown in your face, is something that only you can make the call on. We've lost some friends over the years from melanoma – some were mentors and support when I was running away from it. Their families and friends living with the grief is why I no longer run from this disease, which my wife has named 'Harry'. Sorry to any Harrys reading this.

Going forward, just starting my new journey of being a lab rat again, I know I'm in great hands and have an awesome team of medical and support people around.

The trial is ground-breaking, not just looking at treatment and survival rates like other drug trials; we're chasing a vaccine, and how bloody good would that be?! I know that puts a smile on my face.

Janette Daley

# Janette Daley

I was 37 when the primary melanoma was found on my upper back on 2012.

At 39 (and ¾), I had a baby, and I couldn't understand why my placenta was shipped off to the USA to be dissected and examined, as they mentioned I had a melanoma years before. I now know that you can pass on melanoma to your baby.

I was 41, when it spread through my lymph nodes and there was a lump in my neck.

I was 43, when I was placed in palliative care.

At 48, I am still alive and happy, assisting with a charity, working, travelling, and raising my daughter with my husband. Looking forward to reaching milestones in 2025, i.e. 50th birthday, 20 year wedding anniversary etc.

I'm sharing my story in the hope that everyday Australians will get a skin check as soon as possible. Early detection is key.

I'm a career public servant in Queensland, with over 27 years of service.

Happily married with one child, a daughter.

I like to travel, I have been to the USA and Japan many times, New Zealand, UAE (Dubai), Canada, Turkey, Ireland, United Kingdom, a Contiki through Europe on my honeymoon. With a trip in 2024 to Crete, Greece and Malta.

I have been to every State in Australia, but during covid, we bought a caravan, and we take weekends away throughout the year to create memories.

I love cats, I got my first cat when I was 5 years old, without a cat, I don't feel like it's a home. My first thing I asked my future husband was, I hope you like cats.

## Detection

I had a dark spot just below my shirt line on my back. My husband pointed it out and said it should be checked out as it was black.

I went to a doctor for something else and then I mentioned the spot on my back, the doctor was shocked about how large the spot was (it was similar to a 50-cent coin) and I was referred immediately to the Princess Alexandra hospital (public hospital) in Brisbane to get it cut out.

The initial melanoma was fine, it wasn't until several years later, I had the lump in my throat / right neck, that I had melanoma cancer. I was completely shocked. What followed was surgeries, treatments, side effects, and my life changed forever. My mother and father were completely shaken to the core.

As I looked okay, nobody knew my struggles underneath. I kept strong and I kept on going about my day-to-day activities.

But the side effects were severe, and I had to sell my home in the country as I was too far from the hospital. I moved into town to be closer to the hospital.

When I was really sick in hospital, we didn't tell my daughter how sick I was. I still live with the fear of telling my only child, that mommy might not be here to see her grow up.

I had four surgeries. One surgery was for the primary melanoma and another one to remove further cancerous cells with wide margins.

I had a right neck dissection (also known as cervical lymph node dissection) removing all affected lymph nodes in the neck region. They took over 300 lymph nodes from my neck including some in my face. I was in hospital for one week as I had a drain in the body to remove the fluid. My neck was stiff for a long-time and I still can't turn it properly.

Another surgery was for the removal of my left adrenal gland (adrenalectomy). I was in hospital for two nights and I remember feeling very thirsty and I was not allowed to drink for hours in case I needed to go back into surgery. In the night after the surgery, I made myself get up and go to the toilet, bearing the pain in my stomach, as I knew it was good for recovery.

After each surgery, I generally feel sick and vomit and it takes me a while to recover.

## Targeted therapy

Two weeks after the adrenal gland removal, a PET scan revealed five tumours in my body. As I had a BRAF mutation, I had initial targeted therapy of Debrafenib Trametinib also known as TAF MEK. I had side effects of the rigors (vigorous shaking) and high temperatures over 40 degrees with fevers and sweats, which meant I couldn't take the tablets all the time.

## Immunotherapy

After two months of TAF MEK treatment, a PET scan showed signs of something in my head, so I drove myself to Brisbane Mater private to have an urgent MRI which showed several tumours on my brain. I was then advised I would be undertaking immunotherapy, Nivolumab and Ipilimumab, four times. I only got to two, as I had colitis and was hospitalised twice. On my second hospital visit, I was given another treatment to stop the severe diarrhoea and vomiting. I continued with the Nivolumab when I didn't have side effects and I was having very large dosages of steroids. I had the moon face which is typical of a person having a lot of steroids. I continually had aching joints throughout the whole time of my melanoma journey. As the lungs are suppressed, I had two bouts of influenza A (hospitalised for one) and six chest infections over the time I as on immunotherapy.

## Brain radiation

I also underwent two Gamma Knife radiation treatments. Gamma Knife surgery is a well-established method to treat selected targets in the brain; but it is not a knife. Instead, highly focused beams of radiation are directed to the treatment area in the brain. First treatment was horrendous, the doctor stated due to the timeframe I needed the lightweight frame, which is attached to your head with four pins, preventing your head from moving during imaging and treatment procedures. Local anaesthetic is applied where the pins are to be attached. As I have a needle phobia, this first treatment is seared into my brain as I was terrified. They gave me sedatives which didn't work, but I did sleep through the whole event in the machine. The second treatment, I had the mask and I felt much better. I was awake during the 90-minute treatment, but I felt relieved that I didn't have the attachment on my head. I still have scars on my forehead.

## Targeted therapy

I had a very large tumour grow in my brain and after two seizures, I was stuttering and I couldn't form words, I was given Vemurafenib and Cobimetinib tablets. This is when I needed to take time off work. Within two weeks, I had some serious side effects where my lips and face swelled up and I was placed in hospital. I was in hospital for 2 months as I had a serious allergic reaction to the drugs.

## Hospital / Palliative care

During my time at hospital, I was not able to take more treatments for the cancer. Allergic side effects include but not limited to, skin falling off, fluid on lungs which I felt like I was suffocating, and I had oxygen to breathe which meant I had nose bleeds, my whole body swelled up (I was put in a wheel chair as I couldn't walk), coded as they couldn't find heart beat – I had three surgeries (two PICC lines fell out due to the skin falling off) with a Peripherally Inserted Central Catheters (PICC) line (a PICC line is inserted into a large vein in the arm above the elbow), heart and kidney issues, blurry eyes (couldn't see much), liquid oozing out of my legs, scarring etc.

When I left the hospital, I received care from nurses who came to my house, changed my weeping legs for about two weeks and gave me antibiotics for my staf infection.

My hair fell out after one month after hospital. I empowered myself and took to the shears and did it with a friend.

After this time, I put together a box full of information for my husband, daughter and family. I had pulled together gifts and cards for my daughter for every major milestone, teddy bear with my voice, cards for friends, funeral book for my husband and other information he needed after I passed (such as passwords, bank accounts etc.). That led me to gain strength and get stronger every day.

After 3 months from hospital, I felt well enough to go to work, I told Palliative care that I was well, and they didn't need to contact me.

## Post-palliative care

I had three monthly CT and MRI scans, but in 2023, I am now MRI every six months and one PET or CT scan annually. I have a weekly lymphatic massage with a qualified professional. She has also laser-treated my scars on my legs and arms from the allergic reaction.

## Learnings

Just because I have Trypanophia (fear of needles), a condition marked by irrational, extreme fear of needles, that fear of needles meant I avoided doctors. But I've learnt not to wait to see a doctor, to get to the doctor as soon as possible, even if that means I might have a needle.

I have learnt that everyone's cancer journey is their own to endure. It can sometimes feel very lonely, but by talking with other people with similar experiences, it can a little bit easier.

I have learnt that everyone's journey is different.

I have tried to be very strong throughout my melanoma journey, but it can be very depressing. I don't remember any feelings of hope. But Jay is an inspirational bloke who has survived two cancers and started up a charity to help those who need support, advocates strongly for reduction of melanoma and/or skin cancers.

My advice, if you have been diagnosed with melanoma or another cancer is to breathe, be strong and take along a friend to doctors appointments. As you are shocked by the diagnosis, you might miss what the doctor is saying. Write down your questions, as soon as you get into see the oncologist or radiologist, you might not remember the questions.

Kali Totorica

# Kali Totorica

*By Maria Totorica (Kali's Mum) and Liana Kennedy (Kali's sister)*

We are sharing Kali's story because we would never wish this nightmare on anyone. We want her story to raise awareness, particularly for those who would be identified as low risk and believe that it won't happen to them. Kali loved helping people and we know that by continuing Kali's legacy and sharing her story we can help boost the number of people getting skin checks, and hopefully save lives.

Kali was raised in the small township of Gumlu in North Queensland, on a capsicum farm where she lived with her parents, two older brothers and older sister. She enjoyed the perks of farm life, such as riding quad bikes, and would often make friends with the workers when she was younger. This also helped her to evade doing any of the actual farm work, and being the youngest (and pretty cute) worked in her favour.

Those close to Kali remember her as being a sassy character. She had the most contagious laugh that would make everyone around her smile. Kali loved all things: parties – buying presents, dressing up and having a good time. Kali loved spending time with her family, especially her four nieces (including two god-daughters), two nephews and her dachshund, Tanner. Sadly, Kali did not get to meet her other two nephews that entered the world after she passed, however she did gain another angel niece whom we believe she is caring for in heaven.

Kali was working as a florist, managing her own gifts and flower shop. She had aspirations to grow the business but unfortunately never got the chance. Kali was a very selfless person, she never asked 'Why me?', and instead was worried if her family were also at risk of developing melanoma. After she passed, we found a box of prayers that she had written which were predominantly about her family members achieving their goals and living healthy, happy and prosperous lives. We know that Kali would have loved to fall in love and get married and she would have made an amazing mother.

## Diagnosis

Kali had a mole on her scalp which was not thought to be a concern at previous skin checks. The mole became itchy and one day Kali noticed that it was bleeding. She saw her GP who immediately did a biopsy and later confirmed the diagnosis of melanoma. She was then referred onto a specialist who completed a wide local excision to ensure clear borders on her scalp.

About a year after her initial diagnosis, routine scans identified a recurrence of the melanoma in Kali's neck which again involved surgical excision and lymph node removal.

We celebrated Kali's 21st birthday in September 2018, thinking she was in the all clear and how lucky we were to still have her with us. She then had her first seizure on 25th October, which marked the beginning of a very difficult and emotional ending. An MRI confirmed that the melanoma had metastasised in Kali's brain and we were later informed that she also had leptomeningeal disease. Kali passed away three weeks later.

The diagnosis was devastating though I think we were all still in denial at that time. We were naïve to think that this was something that could be 'fixed' with surgery or treatment and at that stage did not consider that we would be saying goodbye less than two years later.

It was all pretty hard once we realised how serious melanoma was and the reality of it set in. The thought of losing Kali was unbearable. Watching Kali endure side effects of surgery and treatment, having anxiety as we awaited results of scans, feeling guilty and helpless that this was happening to her – the youngest of our immediate family and also our extended family. Yet none of that compares to how difficult it was to walk out of that palliative care room for the last time knowing that we would never see Kali again.

Kali was taking the medications tafinlar and mekinist which came with horrible side effects including fevers, fatigue, headaches, nausea, whole body aches, and consequently disrupted sleep. There were days when Kali couldn't work or even get out of bed because of the severity of the side effects.

But through it all we learnt how bloody tough Kali was, and how precious life is.

Kali was offered involvement in a clinical trial which was investigating whether having radiotherapy, in addition to standard immunotherapy, would reduce the risk of melanoma recurrence. As Kali did not have any detectable melanoma at that stage and was already having immunotherapy, she declined to participate in the trial. Alongside already experiencing side effects of immunotherapy, another consideration for Kali was the risk of losing her hair from the radiation. This may sound vain, however her crazy curls were a defining feature for her and as a young woman, this would have made a huge impact on her self-confidence.

Kali (r) – a last family photo

We tried our best to remain positive but the only real feelings of hope directly related to Kali's journey came after surgeries where it was thought that there was no remaining melanoma. Reading about the journeys of others that Jay shared on social media also instilled a sense of hope, and the support that is generated from the melanoma community that he has created is amazing.

We believe that Kali would like to be remembered for her kind and caring nature, and for the impact she had, whether big or small, on helping to raise awareness of melanoma.

Like all grieving families, we think of Kali every day and reminisce fond memories. We remember her laugh and her cheeky nature. We continue to have a party on her birthday every year with extended family to celebrate the day that she came into our lives. We also host an annual fundraiser, 'Kali's Cup' at the local golf club, where we honour Kali's memory and continue her legacy of raising awareness of melanoma and funds that we forward to the Australian Skin Cancer Foundation to support the continuation of their outstanding work.

If we could give advice about this journey we have been on it is to trust your gut and advocate for yourself when navigating the medical system. It's going to be a rough ride so try to ensure open and honest communication with those close to you and reach out if you need support outside your own network.

We fully believe in the importance of skin checks. Prior to her initial diagnosis, Kali would have identified as very low risk (2% on the MIA risk prediction tool) for melanoma. With a Spanish Father and Italian Mother, dark features and limited sun exposure, Kali did not appear to be someone you would believe to have melanoma. This is why we share her story. Your ethnicity, your age, your occupation – yes, they may affect your risk factor however nobody is immune. We prompt everyone to get regular skin checks because we know the devastation of losing a loved one to this horrible disease.

Jay Allen has single-handedly created a sense of community for a group of people who mostly have never met. Although we did not yet have the pleasure of meeting Jay while Kali was still with us, we know that he and the melanoma community were a huge support for Kali throughout her journey. We, her family, did all we could to help Kali but having the group of people who could relate to what she was going through on a personal level was vital and likely what helped to keep her spirits high. There's a reason that Jay received a Medal of the Order of Australia and that is due to his outstanding achievement and service to the melanoma community. His dedication is remarkable. He is one of the most selfless people that we have ever had the pleasure of meeting and we cannot thank him enough for all that he does.

Drew Sculthorpe

# Drew Sculthorpe

I'm a keen photographer, committed to my role as a public servant. I find immense joy in spending quality time with my beloved wife and daughters, with a special fondness for moments spent by the waterside.

In 2014, my wife first noticed a small mole behind my right ear. Following a biopsy, it was diagnosed as melanoma. Further tests on the margins showed no signs of cancer. Skipping ahead to 2022, most of that year was marked by persistent pain in my left hip. Then, one Saturday afternoon, I suddenly experienced severe rib pain. By Sunday, I felt somewhat better, but by Monday morning, I had a mild fever. Once again, my wife urged me to seek medical help at the Emergency Department. During my visit, scans revealed multiple lesions in various parts of my body, including my hip, liver, lung, femur and spine. Subsequent biopsies confirmed that I had reached stage 4 melanoma. As I began treatment, I received the distressing news that it had also spread to my brain.

How to describe how the news affected me and my loved ones? Total and utter devastation.

At first, we spent a lot of time in what felt like a waiting game – waiting for answers, tests, and appointments. The initial waiting period seemed to drag on endlessly. But once we began meeting with the oncology team and started treatment, things became much brighter. Connecting with others who had faced similar challenges also filled me with hope.

My wife and I decided early on that we would let our 9 and 6-year-old daughters know when we figured out what we were dealing with. That one moment was the toughest thing I've had to do since my diagnosis.

I've been receiving immunotherapy since November 2022. At first, I had four double infusions of nivolumab and ipilimumab, which later changed to a single nivolumab infusion every four weeks. In December 2022, my vision became very blurry, and tests showed that

I had uveitis, an inflammation in the middle layer of the eye. I received treatment with steroid eye drops for several months until it cleared up. In March 2023, I was diagnosed with hyperthyroidism as a side effect of the treatment. I also underwent radiation treatment in September 2023 for to progression of the cancer on my hip.

It's important not to shy away from asking for help or reaching out to those who have already navigated a similar journey before you. Their guidance and support can be invaluable as you tread your own path.

Since meeting Jay Allen at the beginning of 2023, Jay has been an unwavering source of hope and support in my life. His presence and encouragement have played a significant role in uplifting my spirits and helping me navigate through challenging times.

Advocate for Yourself: Be your own advocate in your healthcare journey. Ask questions, seek second opinions if needed, and actively participate in your treatment decisions.

Stay Positive: Maintain a positive outlook, as a positive mindset can contribute to your overall well-being and recovery. This doesn't mean you shouldn't feel upset, angry, or worried. It simply emphasises the importance of maintaining a positive mindset.

Through all of this I've learnt that I'm a lot stronger than I thought I was. And that life is incredibly short and shouldn't be taken for granted.

# Lionel McGuire

*by Sally Everett (daughter)*

When Dad was diagnosed we were so uneducated about melanoma, despite Dad being one of the most sun safe people we knew. We had so much to learn in such a short period of time. We as a family decided to share Dad's story as if we can prevent someone suffering like Dad did and another family having to watch their loved one suffer and feel so useless then that is something we wanted to do.

Dad worked in Local Government for our Local Council, Dubbo Regional Council (he did see a few amalgamations!) for 42 years as a truck driver. Dad was a gentleman, old school and unassuming. He loved a small punt on the races (we would laugh that he was the king of 50 cent each way bets!). He loved his family and adored his two granddaughters.

Dad became very unwell during COVID and we had to send him to hospital. He had a lump on his side that was protruding, similar to a hernia, which we were expecting was what it was. But an MRI discovered a 66 cm internal melanoma compressing on his spine and pelvis.

It was devastating news and it was the hardest thing watching someone you love so much suffer, while feeling so useless. The melanoma was affecting Dad's ability to walk and causing so much pain. He lost so much of his independence, and seeing his frustration was difficult as well. Dad was such a proud man, that being so heavily reliant on others was becoming quite undignified for him, even though we wanted to do what we could to make him as comfortable as we could.

One of the hardest parts of the diagnosis was not knowing much about melanoma, not knowing where to go for support or information. The hospital staff were amazing and looked after us so well, but we wanted information and knowledge and that wasn't easy to find.

At the diagnosis meeting they said if we were having this conversation five years ago it would be very different, things have come so far now. This gave us hope. It is also was a realisation that education about awareness and funds for research and trials are so important, so in another few years the conversations are completely different again.

So I guess we learned that education and prevention is key. There needs to be more awareness. Support services need to be easily accessible, and knowing where to find reliable, information easily.

Melanoma does not discriminate. Anyone can be affected and the statistics are very scary.

Dad received immunotherapy, but only had a couple of treatments before he passed, but it used to make him feel so exhausted.

We remember Dad as being an honest, supportive person who loved his family (but no matter how old you were he would always pull you into line and give you a kick up the backside if you needed it) and gave a good fight. We talk about him all the time, we share photos and stories and our family's work with the ASCF and fulfilling the commitment we made to creating education and awareness. Also our renewed commitment to getting regular skin checks and living a sun safe life, being role models for this and leading by example.

Our Dad will be remembered through all our work we do as a family through the Foundation and as his face travels the country on the Skin Check Truck saving more lives.

Despite the pain, we remember the good times. The funny times. The family holidays. Funny sayings that he used to say and nicknames he had for us – him calling us a Nong Child, no matter how old we were!

If there's advice we could give, it is Don't Suffer Alone. Accept help, seek support. Be open to different treatment ideas and discussions.

Follow Doctors advice! There can be some positive outcomes.

Jay Allen has provided much support and information to our family. We will be forever grateful. He is an inspiration, and his commitment to the Melanoma and Non-Melanoma Skin Cancer Cause is unwavering.

We have met some incredible people that have had positive outcomes, and survival, which is why education and awareness is important.

One key thing we learnt with Dad, and made a pact as a family, if something doesn't look right, or feel right, get it checked.

Prevention is better than a cure. Be sun safe and get regular skin checks.

Lionel McGuire

Bourke family, Hayley front (l)

# Hayley Bourke

*Renee Bourke and Stephen Bourke*

Hayley wanted to spread her message far and wide, to help educate in hopes to prevent others going through what she did

Hayley had an infectious smile. She loved experimenting with make-up – watching endless YouTube tutorials to get new ideas – and nailed it every time. She loved wearing bright colours, had a huge wardrobe (as a result of her online shopping addiction), and sported many different styles.

Hayley and her friends loved a night of karaoke, with her favourites being Rhianna's 'Please Don't Stop the Music', Bon Jovi's 'Livin'on a Prayer' and The Foundation's 'Build Me Up Buttercup'. If she wasn't singing the night away, she was the last one on the dance floor. Hayley was so much fun to be out with.

Hayley loved her rescue greyhound, Gracie (who had a bigger wardrobe than her) and she always put others before herself. People always described Hayley as bubbly, selfless and kind.

Hayley grew up in Sydney with her parents Sandra and Stephen, and her sister, Renee who was born only 10 months after Hayley. Irish twins. Hayley and Renee shared a deep connection where they often had the same thought, at the same time, knew each other's opinion without voicing it, and would spontaneously sing the same lyric (often incorrectly) at the exact same time out of nowhere. Many car-eoke sessions were had over the years.

With Hayley's diagnosis came a mission to spread awareness about melanoma and to change the idea of a tan looking better than having pale skin. This was the result of growing up in Australia and the idea of a 'bronzed Aussie' being desired and ingrained in us. Although Hayley would never lay out in the sun, she did use fake tan. She used it before realising that she was promoting the exact idea she was trying to change. A bottled tan is better than a sun tan, but accepting the skin you're in is better than both.

When Hayley was 21 years old, she bumped a mole on her left shoulder blade and it hurt, so she showed her mum who then took her to the doctors to have it checked out. After getting the mole biopsied, it came back as melanoma, stage 2. She then had a wider incision and two lymph nodes removed to see how far it had spread. The following five years consisted of regular visits to the cancer clinic until they were happy that Hayley was all clear – which they diagnosed.

Five years on, Hayley felt a lump under her left armpit, and her heart sank. She went to the doctors and ended up having an operation to remove the lymph nodes from under her arm for testing, many of which came back cancerous. After further scans, they found that melanoma had also spread to her ovaries, pancreas and kidney. This was now stage 4 melanoma.

At first, it was shock. You're not sure what to say, yet you have so many questions. You wonder and hope that there's a chance they got this wrong, but then you see the scans and the evidence of black spots all throughout the body. It's heartbreaking and hard to accept. You think of all the things they haven't experienced yet, and question if you've done everything you can, and lived every moment to the fullest. You wonder how much time you have left with your loved one and question how on earth can you go on living every day without this person in your life.

Hayley was quite open about her story and was more worried about everyone else and how her diagnosis was affecting them. The treatments Hayley underwent had a variety of side effects, with the most frustrating being clouded vision, feeling nauseous, weight fluctuations and feeling lethargic. It is hard to put in 100%, when you're feeling 30% of your regular self.

But the hardest part of the diagnosis was coming to terms that her disease was terminal – the realisation that the diagnosis is life threatening and the thought that Hayley probably wouldn't reach her forties.

And there was confusion regarding medications and treatments.

And we are still in disbelief nearly a year after her passing.

Hayley had several types of targeted treatments, many different immunotherapies, combination therapies, several radiation sessions, too many biopsies to remember, and 14 operations. It was tiring, frustrating, overwhelming, but at the same time, Hayley was hopeful.

And sometimes, hope is all you have to hold on to throughout.

Hope that there will be a medical breakthrough or a miracle.

Quite often there would be a glimmer of hope after tests or scans showed a reduction in the size or spread of the tumours, only to reverse that trend after a period of time.

Hayley was part of a clinical trial, which gave her hope and she was very positive it would work. She would always be the first to put her hand up to try something new. And when it didn't, investigating if other trials were available. Always wishing and praying something new was available

The side effects of medication brought other issues to deal with. Nausea, diarrhoea, stiffness and skin rashes.

We learned a lot from the experience. The importance of being sun safe, the power of social media and the importance of what we promote on it, especially to young impressionable people. And making sure you surround yourself with love and the things that make you happy. We need to look after our bodies, because they are the vessels we've been given to inhabit. Live a full life, because this can happen to anyone at any time.

We remember Hayley for her support of others going through this terrible journey. She responded to those people even if she was having a hard time herself. She lost many of her friends which was extremely hard for her.

We remember her bravery, honesty, dedication to her friends and family and love of life.

We remember Hayley's selflessness; being more concerned for others than herself. And the sadness of someone in their 30s putting their affairs in order to help the ones left behind … Her discussions with family members about her funeral.

We remember also her determination to get the message out there for sun safe practices, especially to young females who follow beauty trends and tan.

We remember and honour Hayley by keeping her name alive. We talk about her a lot and encourage others to also. Although we are

Hayley and Isabel

grieving and will grieve for Hayley for the rest of our lives, we want to talk about her and encourage others to if they want to. It keeps her memory alive, and we love hearing about the experiences others have had with her.

I remember how much fun it was growing up with a sister, and how lucky we all are having shared our life with her for 37 years.

## ASCF

Hayley loved and believed so deeply in Jay Allen and his mission. His heart is in the right place and he gives everything he has, to others. Despite fighting his own battles, he is always there for everyone else, and Hayley and our whole family would have been lost throughout this journey, if it wasn't for Jay.

Having support through your journey, is so important. Don't be afraid to reach out. Seek others who have experienced something similar and be there for each other. Don't be hesitant to choose where you put your time and energy in.

As yet, there is no perfect treatment, but everyone is different. If the treatment you are on doesn't work, be assured we have the world's leading experts here in Australia, working full time on this mongrel disease.

# Lissy Malcolm

*By Renee, Lissy's twin sister*

Before my life changed, I would sometimes hear people say that life can change forever in just one moment. How the life we know is so fragile. Don't take anything for granted they would say. Live in the 'now'.

I don't know who 'they' are, but 'they' were right. One moment can change it all. One moment. I look back now and realise that I used to take my life 'before' for granted. If only I could turn back time. All the times I had driven past my sister's place and not called in. Those times I tried to catch up with her for coffee and we were both busy, that's OK, another time. Sometimes 'another time' never comes.

It was just an ordinary Monday afternoon. I had picked the kids up from school and was getting on with cooking dinner. Being the last week of November, and the last week of school before Christmas holidays, everything was beginning to have that pre-holidays relaxed feel. My mind was drifting to thoughts of Christmas as I was stirring dinner. Beef Stroganoff.

I remember every detail of that afternoon.

My thoughts were interrupted by my mobiles message tone.

Mum.

What did Mum want? I had spoken with her that morning. 'Have you spoken to Lis today?' Instantly worried about my sister, I replied … What? Why? What's wrong? Yes, I was messaging with Lis that morning, our conversation was nothing out of the ordinary. What could have happened between now and then? My mind was racing.

Mum replied that Lis been to the doctor because she was getting episodes of shortness of breath. What? What!!!! Wait… For how long? Why didn't she tell me? She sounded OK this morning? Maybe she had a cold and it went to her chest? Picked up something from the hospital where she worked? Why did she not mention any of this to me?(I knew before I even finished asking myself the question, she didn't want to worry anyone) *mind panicking* … The doctor had sent

185

her for an x-ray and made another appointment to return the following day for the results.

The x-ray showed massive left sided pleural effusion. *what?*! Why would that happen? Even though it's not usual protocol, the X-ray nurse had discussed the result with Lis as it was late in the afternoon and she knew that Lis wasn't going to see her doctor for the results until the next day. She said if things got worse to go straight to Emergency. My mind desperately searched my knowledge base for non-malignant causes of unilateral effusions, but it wasn't coming up with much. I had previously worked in x-ray, so I knew immediately that this was not good. My stomach turned … filled with nerves and tied itself in knots.

No beef stroganoff for me that night.

Mum was going through all other possibilities, maybe an infection, unilateral pneumonia, but my mind went straight to our worst fears.

I said, 'What about her melanoma from four years ago Mum, could it have spread?' I wanted Mum to message back and say something positive like she usually did like 'don't be silly, they caught it early, it was four years ago', but she didn't. She messaged back: I think our girl is in trouble. *I think our girl is in trouble.* I still remember those words and how they scared me to my core. To this day, I still think about those words. If Mum and I were both in agreeance about what the diagnosis could be, then that makes it a real possibility. *Denial, lets stay there until we know.* After all, I wasn't a doctor, what did I know?

What was ahead for our family. For my sister's family? My thoughts instantly went to my 14-year-old niece and my 10-year-old nephew. Sure, there were a number of other things it could be, but we had to be real, to mentally prepare.

Once I had spoken to Lis, I felt a bit better. She was tough, she sounded ok. She decided not to keep her GP appointment for the following day as she knew that she would just be sent to an ED department. So, the next morning, once her kids were at school, her husband drove her to the nearest large hospital. My mind often drifts to that morning, how did she feel being driven to that hospital? Knowing what the possibilities were. I was glued to my phone the whole day. Heart racing every time it buzzed or rang. Not her. Didn't hear from her until that night.

Once the ED doctors had x-rayed her again, they realised they needed to urgently drain the effusion for her. The effusion was so large that the fluid was displacing her heart. Over the next 3 days, they drained 3L of fluid from her left pleural space. I went to visit her on the Thursday afternoon/evening. She looked surprisingly good. *Thank god. cause if she looked sick, I would have gone to shit.* She was desperate to have her hair washed. So, there we were, her and I, in the shower in her hospital room, me washing her hair, trying not to get my clothes wet, and tyring to not trip on her lung drain. Side buddy as she called it. We actually had a laugh at how life can change so quickly. The week before, we had been catching up for a coffee and now I was washing her hair in hospital. Cannot comprehend that.

The doctors performed x-rays and scans looking for the cause of the effusion.

They found it.

Extensive pleural metastases. From what primary, they didn't know.

I knew.

She had an enlarged lymph node in her right armpit, perfect for biopsy. From that they found the culprit.

Melanoma.

From the Stage 1B melanoma she had excised four years previously. Statistically very unlucky. The start of the 'bad luck' as I saw it. Statistically she should have never been bothered by that melanoma again. This was the opinion of many of the doctors and specialists we encountered along Lis's journey. *So yes, this was all very unfair.* I tried to make sense of 'why her' in my mind. I still can't to this day.

Funnily enough, I remember feeling happy that it was melanoma because I had just heard on the news about all these amazing breakthroughs in treatment for melanoma. The news didn't say that the 'miracle' doesn't happen for everyone, that some patients are 'super progressors' or 'non responders'. The news didn't say that melanoma is a sneaky, tricky, relentless bastard.

Through the whole diagnosis process, Lis was nothing short of amazing. She just took every piece of information with bravery and only had concern for her family and how we were handling it. I remember she messaged me late on the day she was diagnosed, and she said 'Nay, I just want you to know that I am OK. Please don't worry about me. This is the path I am meant to be on for whatever reason. I am going to take each day as it comes and make the most of the time I have left. So please don't cry or be worried about me. I have already accepted this. I love you.'

I know she intended to make me feel better, but I think I actually cried more because of how brave she was. She had so much ahead of her.

She was discharged about 4 days after they diagnosed her. She was feeling a bit unwell still but managed to function at home. She was researching and doing everything she could to be healthier for her fight. She started juicing and using essential oils. She tried some Yoga too but had to be careful about not over-exerting herself. Both she and I started doing a lot of reading and research. All statistics on stage 4 melanoma were not very nice, so we stayed away from google for a while. *Hate Google!!* At 2am when awake in the middle of the night, my mind mysteriously used to go straight to those statistics. *Of course!*

She was referred to a renowned Professor at the PA Hospital in Brisbane for treatment. The best of the best all of my research said. *That's who we need for our girl!* Her appointment was in early January 2018, and it couldn't come fast enough.

We had Christmas together, and Lis was feeling well on the day, she had been suffering badly from nausea on and off since being discharged from hospital so we were happy she could relax and enjoy Christmas with us. It really was a lovely day; the family was all together. I remember again being in awe of my big sis, she was so happy and accepting that day. She even enjoyed a glass of bubbles with us. For just a split second, everything felt normal again. Just for a tiny second. But as I looked at everyone else's faces around the table I could see the question on their faces, in their eyes ... Is this Lis's last Christmas with us? Please no.

The day came for her appointment at the PA. We were so hopeful and eager to hear what the professor had to say. The official diagnosis – Stage 4B BRAF+ metastatic melanoma. Lis was offered 2 treatment options.

1. Targeted therapy – short story – a temporary fix. Will stop working eventually but could give her years longer, possibly 3 years.

2. Bristol-Myers Squibb Clinical Trial. An unknown drug in combination with Nivolumab.

Of course, she chose the Clinical Trial, after all, that's where all the miracles happen. Daily oral tablets, which was the unknown drug, and a monthly infusion of Nivolumab. 2 years. That made me feel good, they must think she will still be here in 2 years. We were so optimistic, so happy that she was in good hands.

This mystery tablet really knocked her around. Nausea and vomiting. Not nice. So hard to find relief. She ended up in ED again and again to receive an anti-vomiting injection and for some re-hydration. This seemed to go on and on with little relief. We tried everything!!! Finally read on a melanoma support group to try Nausicalm.

It worked!!! We were so happy that she was finally able to eat and get a good night sleep. Things that were taken for granted before, like going to bed, or having breakfast, now became a big deal in her life. Getting good rest was rare, she had to sleep half sitting up and that combined with her nausea, was not great for sleep. Over 4 weeks she had lost over 10kg. She said it wasn't a diet she would recommend trying. Still had her sense of humour. I told her I had lost 4kg, while not as effective as the 'I have melanoma and the drugs saving me make me vomit' diet, the 'worrying sister' diet was still working. We had always thought we were pretty hilarious with our jokes.

She had her first infusion of Nivolumab no problems at all. What a relief. We had all sorts of positive mental pictures about her next lot of scans! We were ready for our miracle. Mum and Dad, who lived 530km away had been visiting constantly, helping out where they could. It was hard for them being so far away. As soon as Lis was diagnosed, they made a decision to move to Qld.

Second month into the trial. Nausea and vomiting back with a vengeance. After spending a Thursday night in ED in Beaudesert Hospital getting anti-vomiting drugs, she was back to the PA on Friday for her Nivolumab infusion. She sure was a trooper and nothing was stopping her getting her Nivo she said! This time, things did not go as well as her first infusion. She had a reaction. Back pain and shortness of breath and skyrocketing blood pressure. Apparently, this was common, to have a reaction to the second infusion, and the lovely staff knew just what to do. We were thankful that Lis was able to have her second infusion once she had recovered from the reaction, they just reduced the infusion rate.

Back home later that night, Lis was telling me that she still didn't feel quite right, and that her shortness of breath was being troublesome again. I told her I would check in on her the following day.

She was still no better the next day and was ordered back to the PA emergency. After more scans and tests, it was discovered that her cancer had been quite busy during the 8 or so weeks since diagnosis. It had significantly progressed and was now all around both pleura, causing a right sided pleural effusion. All of the doctors and oncologist were shocked at how quickly things had progressed. This pissed me off more than I can describe. Why the hell was her cancer so aggressive? She deserved to stay on this clinical trial so she could have her miracle. This also scared the shit out of me. We could not take our eye off the ball even for a moment. I totally didn't trust her cancer at all. It was behaving so strangely. If it was so aggressive, why was it only attacking her pleura? I imaged an aggressive melanoma would spread everywhere else. Not hers. Why??

So, she had a right sided drain put in to drain the fluid. During this hospital stay, she was sick. I mean, really sick. I remember one day walking into her room and seeing her like that, just hit me. She's a cancer patient. This was the first time she looked like a cancer patient. It made me so so sad. The girl that had been my best friend my whole life, the girl that knew all my worst fears and biggest dreams, and I knew hers, was a cancer patient, and things weren't looking good.

Professor was away during this hospital stay and her fill-in was discussing things with Lis. This doctor said that things didn't look good, that Lis was off the trial due to her oxygen needs and she should try targeted therapy. Of course, we were all very upset. This 'Targeted Therapy' is the one that stops working isn't it? Why would we want her to swap onto the drug that eventually stops working? So, what are they telling us, we are going for just more time, not a cure? This cannot be happening. We were clinging to the idea and hope that our miracle was waiting to happen because of that trial, and now that was taken away.

I think this was the first time we saw what her cancer was capable of in a short time and it scared us. During the end of that hospital stay, Professor returned and had a consult with Lis in her hospital room. She was still so optimistic, it made us feel better. She said that yes, Lis was off the trial, due to her being on oxygen. And yes, she would move onto Targeted Therapy, which would work extremely quickly, and she would be off oxygen within the week. Then at the right time we would swap to immunotherapy for long term treatment. Long-term. I loved those words. Sounded like a good plan to us. This other fill in doctor caused the whole family so much pain and grief, we were so glad that Professor Atkinson was back and that she explained things a lot clearer.

Professor was right, Lis was better very quickly. That Targeted Therapy is amazing and worked its magic. After a few days she was spending up to 8 hours off oxygen with saturation levels of 97%. Lis got back to life, looking after her kids, visiting me, shopping. It was wonderful. Life went back to a semi-normal phase. Lis was coming for coffee again, we were doing lunch, chatting about non cancer things … I remember that I was able to think about other things in life, without the 'Your sister has cancer' song playing in the background constantly.

In March, she had progress scans. Her tumours had 'significantly shrunk', no effusion. The rest of her body and brain were still clear. We were beyond happy. I remember the knot that had been in my stomach since December the year before, released a little. The tears this day were happy tears.

Unfortunately, the good news didn't last very long. Her steroid dose was high, and it was thought it should be reduced. Lis was worried about tapering off as she knew that it was her steroids that were keeping her feeling well. Within 24 hours of being off steroids, she was in trouble. High fevers, vomiting and nausea. So sick that a prescription for steroids had to be faxed to our local pharmacy. How ridiculous I thought, taking her off, putting her on, just leave her on them if that's what she needs to feel well…

From that point on, she never really got back on top of her side effects, especially the fevers from her Targeted Therapy. So, for the month of April, she was off treatment more than she was on treatment. I was so worried about this because we all knew she had aggressive melanoma and just how fast it had taken over her lungs before. Professor had even referred to her as a 'Super Progressor'. Scary. Her next lot of scans showed slight progression. It was decided to wait and see what happened over the next month, to see if the targeted therapy would kick back in and do its thing. What? Run that by me again…wait and see??? It just didn't make sense to me! I felt like we were taking our eyes of the ball big time. 'Wait and see' and aggressive cancer should never be in the same sentence.

I remember chatting with Lis on the morning of her check-up in June. She knew something was happening in her body. She felt like things were progressing quickly again. She felt that her targeted therapy had stopped working, after only a few months. Some people get a few years from it!!! I was hoping it was just that she was off it more than on it, and that she could be placed on a higher dose of steroids and continue on, uninterrupted and that it would do its thing again. I had all the ideas!! Lis used to call me her Team Leader. And in a way, I was. Lis went in optimistic that Professor would still have a number of options up her sleeve. After all, she was the best of the best.

So, her appointment with Professor was something I will never forget until the day I take my last breath. After more tests and scans, she was told her cancer had progressed rapidly. Well of course it did. The previous plan of 'swapping to immunotherapy at the right time' was out the door. She didn't have enough time for immunotherapy to start working before her cancer would take her. She was told 'Get your affairs in order, go home and write letters to your loved ones, this will catch you'. There were some other treatments we could try but because of the state of her lungs, there was absolutely no room for error, every day was crucial. She moved onto another type of targeted therapy. Weekly LDH levels (like a cancer marker) to see if it was working. My head was spinning. Four months if the treatments didn't work. That was October. Please don't do this.

I gave Lis space to process … that was so hard, I just wanted to run to her, make everything better for her. But I couldn't. No-one could. She had just been told she was dying by one of the best melanoma specialists in Australia. To say we were devastated would be an understatement. I was a mess. I couldn't comprehend. I had so much regret that I didn't make Lis fight against the 'wait and see' plan a few months previously. I was just hoping and praying that these last treatments would offer some hope.

First LDH, lower! So relieved. Next LDH, stable. Not ideal. Next LDH rising again. Off targeted and onto Ipi/Nivo combination. The big guns in melanoma treatments.

These big guns put her in hospital again, severe vomiting. But luckily this was her quickest visit yet, just needed some IV steroids and she was out. Professor decided to apply for a third type of targeted therapy only available in France, through compassionate access. It was granted and the drugs were sent. Professor was throwing everything she had at Lis's melanoma.

After her second ipi/nivo treatment, Lis was fine. We were so happy that she only felt a little fatigued, especially after the last treatment put her in hospital and also happy that her LDH remained stable. Lis and I were so sure that this was a sign that it was working. It had to be a sign that it was working. We just couldn't comprehend the alternative. We had our talks and chats about it though and I am still in awe of how brave Lis was in facing her own death. My hero. No one will ever replace her in that role.

After her third ipi/nivo things went a bit downhill. Liver levels were super high and LDH on the rise again. Please give us a break!!!! Let us have some good news …

Clinically Lis deteriorated and was finding it hard to breathe more than usual. Oh no, I was thinking, what's happening now? I remember her ringing to tell me she might go to ED. I kept thinking, wow, Lis avoids ED, so she must be feeling very sick. This was just after her 45th birthday.

The doctors weren't sure what was happening with her, her sats were low, but her scans were stable. Perhaps pneumonitis. Professor thought perhaps her disease was progressing, but scans were not showing it yet. I refused to believe that. *Refused*. If it wasn't showing on the scans, it wasn't happening in my book!!! She improved somewhat and was discharged. Though again, she never really got back to where she was before admission.

Back at home, she was spending more and more time in bed, she was sick. Mum and I were doing what we could to help her and the family. Mum and Dad had sold their house in NSW and were moving up soon. Lis was happy about this. Lis was aware of the impact her illness was having on the family. She was always worried about us and not herself. Amazing. Her son was a big WWE fan, and she booked a family getaway in October to Melbourne to see a show. I was so happy she did that, not only was it a big F-you to her 'expiry date', a nice family get away is what she needed, now she just had to get off oxygen and get well enough to get there!! Her lungs never really did recover well from the pneumonitis.

She was doing well enough to be booked for her 4th ipi/nivo infusion, but first, she had to reduce the steroid dose she was taking, she was on 75mg a day and had to get down to below 10mg before they would consider infusing her. She was tapering off slowly when her colitis symptoms started. It was so severe, her vomiting and diarrhoea was so bad, she told me she wanted to give up. Now Lis was a stubborn Leo and she *never* gives up. She tried everything she was told to try. Nothing worked. Time had come for Mum and Dad to move into their new house, only five minutes from Lis's house. She was looking forward to helping them unpack, so she was trying her hardest to stay out of hospital. But it all got too much, her latest blood work wasn't great. LDH rising again and her red cells were very low. She needed a red cell transfusion. Back to hospital. She was not happy. We were not happy. She missed out on unpacking. We were optimistic that possibly it was her low red cells that was causing her worsening shortness of breath. So, in a way, I was happy that she was back in hospital so she could get the red cells and her breathing would improve. Her breathing always scared me, and I guess I used it as a gauge as to how she was travelling.

So back in hospital again, she said she felt a bit better and wanted to come home. She had a red cell transfusion and also IV steroids for her colitis. She felt somewhat her old self again. However, her shortness of breath lingered. It did not improve with the transfusion as I had hoped. Doctors thought she may have caught hospital acquired pneumonia and ordered a CT scan of her chest.

I remember talking to her after she had the scan. We were both so optimistic that her cancer hadn't progressed. Her LDH was a little high but stable, her previous scans had shown her to be stable as well. But it was the next day when she got the results that would shatter us all.

This disease that she had fought so hard to beat for 9 months was going to win. I still remember her text. 'Good morning Nay, I hate to blurt this out in a text message, but I can't talk right now. My shortness of breath was not pneumonia. It is significant disease progression. Treatment is not working. There is nothing more they can do and I they say I won't see Christmas. I will be on permanent oxygen from now on. Can you please call Mum because she just sent a message to find out how I am'?

Just like that. Another message. Tore my heart out. That call to Mum was one of the hardest things I have had to do. We were all just absolutely devastated. We spent that day together. Not saying much but just being together. I was trying to get my mind ready to lose my sister. It didn't work. I remember saying to Mum that we only get one chance at this, I know this is a shitty shitty situation, but we will only support her at the end of her life once, one chance. Let's make her time left about love, comfort, caring and beautiful memories. We will have the chance to cry and rage later.

That night Lis was discharged from hospital. She was sick, she was tired, she was on oxygen, she was scared, she was sad. I was sad. Shattered to be exact. I know just how much she wanted to, and needed, to beat this, we had many long talks about it. I couldn't believe it. We were all in shock.

The following day, which was a Thursday, the palliative care team came out to her house. They took us all through the chart of drugs and told us how to care for her. It was October 4th and until then we had in our mind that we had her until Christmas. The palliative care nurse said we should prepare ourselves for it to be sooner than that. This bastard of a disease was not only cutting off her air, it was cutting off blood vessels in her lungs and it was also in her pericardial space, around her heart. So, we were told then that it could be the weekend. The weekend was 2 days away. 2 days. I was numb, I felt sick. How the hell do you surrender? That's how it felt. I couldn't surrender. This is my sister. My only sister.

I wrote her a letter. I cannot describe the pain I felt that day, sitting at the keyboard in my office trying to say goodbye to my sister. The kids were on school holidays and were coming in and out of the office. I was trying to hide what was going on. Their view of the world was still all sunshine and golden. I wasn't ready for them to experience the scary, sickness unfair part. I wanted to filter the information to them in an age appropriate way, but I needed time to process it before I talked to them.

Back to the letter. I decided I was refusing to say goodbye. We would still be sisters, and I would watch over things from down here, and she would watch over things from up there. We would still be as close as ever. I would talk to her and she would hear me. She would let me know she was near, and I would know it was her. I promised her all of these things and promised I would look after her beautiful kids. Gosh I hope those words comforted her in some way.

It just so happened that the weekend that was approaching was the weekend that she had booked for her family to head to Melbourne for the wrestling. She pleaded with her husband to please still take the kids. So, he did, reluctantly. It made Lis so happy that they were off on an adventure and far away from witnessing her sickness.

It was arranged that Lis would stay with Mum and Dad at their new house for the weekend that her family was in Melbourne and I was going around to stay too, to help Mum look after her and to just be together. I arrived about lunchtime on Friday and Lis was set up at the window in a recliner, looking out over Mum and Dads back gardens. She was on oxygen, but still looked Ok. I remember trying to sweep in there like a breath of fresh air, acting normal, cracking my jokes as usual, with extra make-up on so you couldn't tell I'd been crying for 24 hours straight. I don't know why I did that? Why was I so scared to let her know I was destroyed and terrified? I sometimes think now how heartless I must have looked to her, to be seemingly carrying on as normal. But then I realised she would have known. She would have known that was me, showing her, I would be OK and that she could go peacefully, without the burden on her soul of destroying my life or changing me so much that I wouldn't recognise myself. So as much as I don't like to admit it, I was cheerful and my normal self, someone who didn't give her sister the chance to talk of her fears or wishes about the journey ahead. At this stage though, I thought we had time, well days anyway, not hours.

We were talking, laughing, telling stories. I massaged her swollen ankles and feet for an hour or so. My mind said 'her kidneys are shuttng down' I told my mind to shut up. I learned all of her drug regimes and was determined to give her everything she needed to remain pain free and happy. I made Lasagne for dinner and she managed to eat a little of that and really enjoyed it. I remember thinking that she was ready to go because she just seemed so at peace with everything. She gave me all of her perfume that she wouldn't get to use. How is she so strong...? hold it together Renee!!

She showered herself, which was amazing given how sick she was. She was a very private person, so I was dreading the day she would need to be showered. We tucked her into bed that night and gave her a dose of hydromorphone as she had some pain and was a bit breathless.

The night that followed, I'll never forget. Lis needed us. She needed drugs. All of the drugs. Her pain and breathlessness were increasing all the time. *You bastard melanoma, I hate you.* I was never so grateful that Mum was a nurse. In the end we were giving her hourly doses of whatever we could to keep her comfortable. We worked so well together as a team to take care of our girl that night.

The next morning, we knew it was time to send her to Palliative Care in Beaudesert Hospital (she didn't want to pass at home). She was no longer conscious, and her breathing was quite shallow. So, we called the ambulance and she was transported to hospital. She didn't even wake up. *It was pouring rain as the ambulance drove away from the house – the world was crying.* Mum went in the ambulance with her and Dad and I followed in the car.

On Saturday 6th October 2018, she was admitted to the Jacaranda Room at the Beaudesert Hospital. The staff there were so lovely and respectful of her. They also looked after Mum's needs too, as Mum stayed with her. She woke up again for a few hours and she was pain free, probably high on drugs, but she was cracking jokes all the time. Stirring us all up as she used to do. What a gift that was to all of us. They say how you are in life, you are in death, and that was how she was. Funny. Loving. Cheeky.

She hung on until Sunday 7th October, she opened her eyes, looked at Mum, who said it was OK to go, and then she was gone. 6.21pm. She went so peacefully and with so much grace. We were so proud of her.

My mind drifts to the Ed Sheeran lyrics 'Spread your wings, and I know that when God took you back, he said Hallelujah you're home'

Words cannot express how much my heart and soul shattered in that moment. Can you prepare for it? No. Even though we knew it was coming. The reality is so so different. I was surrounded by so many amazing supportive people, I was so lucky.

Lis wanted a private memorial service. So that's what she had. Just very close family. I wore her favourite top of mine, and her perfume.

'Somewhere Over the Rainbow', 'Amazing Grace' and 'The Last Goodbye' were her songs. It was raining heavily the day of her service. She loved rain. It rained all day.

As I sit here now typing this, I have lived almost 6 months on this earth without my sister. Some days she feels far away. Some days she is near. I feel her presence. She has sent many signs and I have noticed them, just like I promised in my letter. Some days, the thought of her being gone still literally takes my breath away. Some days are hard, and I am angry. Some days are better, and I am happy. So many ups and downs. One thing I do know, I will live my best life for her. I am not there yet, I don't know how long it will take me to be there, but I will do it. *For her.*

I miss her humour. I miss her theories and wisdom. I miss her amazing laugh. I still go to text her sometimes. I stare at her photos, my brain trying to get my heart to accept that she is gone. My heart still won't believe. Won't accept.

Not sure it ever will.

Not sure I want it to.

Lissy Malcolm (l) and Renee (r)

Tess McGowan-Chan and Raph McGowan

# Tess McGowan-Chan

*Raphael McGowan (brother)*

Tess is my older sister by 2 years. Her birthday is March 13 and mine is March 17.

In our family there is Mum and Dad, and my siblings are:

- (Eldest) Jeremiah (brother)
- Tess
- (me) Raphael
- Iggy (brother)
- Miriam (sister)
- Dominica (sister)
- Collette (sister)

Tess was a beautiful soul who gave so much happiness to everyone she would meet. Her story, the selflessness she displayed from the time she was diagnosed to her passing needs to be shared. As an example, and as a way that her husband and daughter can always read and be reminded of.

I have personally taken on the gift of continuing Tess's legacy, on behalf of all those that knew her. I am honoured to be able to do this and find ways to share her name, stories and photos. She continues to inspire today.

Tess loved to have fun and she had a beautiful smile! She loved singing, playing guitar, acting, theatre and sport. She excelled at both basketball and netball. She'd always let Dad know if on a weekend he was watching us boys play sport more than the girls, just to keep it even as she wanted them part of it.

What Tess didn't like was hostility between people. She could sense it and worked until it was resolved. This was at home and at school. She did this because she said she didn't want precious time wasted.

Tess was a very intelligent person! Always top of her class at school and university. She started doing a business degree and was getting High Distinctions. But then she told us that she didn't love business, but she loved music and acting more and this is what she wanted to pursue.

I've always remembered this example she set – to follow your passion. Even though it was a tough road for Tess. But just before her diagnosis she reached a point of singing classical music with the conservatorium of music, performing on stage in multiple plays, and recording music. Tess said her greatest gift was being a mother to Mabel.

**From Igg**

Tess possessed an extraordinary passion, sensitivity, and nurturing nature. Her unconditional love and unwavering support were constants in her character. Her remarkable empathy gravitated towards the underprivileged and those facing difficulties. Additionally, Tess exhibited an intense enthusiasm for singing, music, theatre, and self-expression.

**From Collette**

Tess's personality was selfless, kind and compassionate.

She always held space for everyone to simply feel any emotion or share and ideas no matter how small or large.

Tess had one of the most beautiful and unique abilities to see every situation from a different perspective. She always saw the best in people.

Tess went after every dream she ever had. The bigger, wild and crazy it seemed she did whatever it took to achieve. 'Do it your way baby'

That's what she would always say Going after a big wild goal.

She won so many scholarships and awards because she believed in herself, her idea, her talent and went for it.

Tess was the definition of a great friend. She had friendships that were over 20 years old full of love, laughter, support and memories. You could always count on Tess to be the most loyal and loving friend.

## From Dominica

Tess had the most cosy, loving, understanding and intelligent energy. Tess was 10 years older than me and had the best big sister presence to me!

Tess just loved every family member so much and allowed people to express themselves. All the sisters would sit around together, first thing in the morning in our PJs and late at night in the hallway. And chat for so long. Tess to me is an open heart, that feels like a well-worn nighty with your favourite character on it. You feel cosy, safe and you believe in magic! That is Tess to me. I feel my relationship has developed with Tess, so much over the years, even after she had moved into the spiritual realm. As I pray and chat to her everyday. I feel her so close and see her personality and essence through her daughter Mabel. I laugh so much with Mabel and have such a familiar feeling with her, that is the same as Tess and I. Mabel is so loving, intelligent and full of magic. And Tess is so proud of her I know! As Mabel says, 'Mummy is watching from up above'.

Tess was married in November, 2010 to Victor Chan, a doctor and anaesthesiologist. They had such an incredible connection, both emotionally and physically. They were a perfect match.

*The following is a summary of Tess's treatment given by her husband Victor*

## Victor

In April 2011, Tess became pregnant with their first child and four months later Victor discovered a mole on Tess's back had changed. This led to having a skin check and the earth-shattering diagnoses of Stage 3 melanoma. At this time, it was regarded as a cancer that was only curable with surgery. That meant people with stage 1-3 melanoma who had surgery that got all the cancer had a greater chance of cure. For stage 3 patients, chemotherapy was not routinely offered after surgery as it is for other cancer because there was not strong evidence for it helping in melanoma. So any treatments during pregnancy like conventional chemo were never discussed with Tess and Victor because that was not what was done for melanoma at the time. It was really just for stage 4 patients.

The surgery involved a wide local excision of the area where the melanoma was and also had a removal of the lymph nodes in her axilla (underarm). Tess never had any scans to exclude stage 4 melanoma because she was pregnant at the time. It was not offered by the surgeon and we did not explore this at the time on his advice.

August 2011. When she was found to have stage 4 metastatic melanoma late in the pregnancy (these were the breast lumps that were biopsied), Tess had an induction of labour so that Mabel could be delivered and she could then start on treatment. When she did start, she had conventional chemotherapy treatment which was not effective and then had immunotherapy with a drug called Yervoy (Ipilimumab), but unfortunately this was not effective either. Her oncologist wanted to enrol her in a new drug trial but she became too unwell to have the treatment.

During her chemo treatments Tess had the problem of fluid around the lung (pleural effusion), which was drained once, but reaccumulated so she had surgery to prevent it building up again. After the surgery she started experiencing significant pain issues around her chest and had to be on significant pain meds to manage this.

For myself, Raph, reading this takes me right back. When a loved one is going through this it is all that matters. The daily life and world that existed before disappears. Tess's health became the number one priority in all our lives.

This is a very important part of Tess's story as it reinforces the most valued thing to her – family.

Tess's diagnosis sent shockwaves through the whole family. We had no history of melanoma, so it was a devastating first for us. After Tess was given the news, our family dropped everything to rally around her and Victor. Shortly after, when Mabel was born, we were there to help with anything she or Victor needed.

When I was told of the news that Tess had melanoma, I was in the United States, back in 2011. Day 66 days of an adventure with two mates, cycling across the country. It was about 7am and we were packing up our tents. We only had one phone and when my friend answered it he said 'Raph, it's for you, it's your Dad'. I immediately knew something was wrong. Dad had never called duding this trip.

He cut straight to it and said that Tess had a skin check, a mole removed and it was melanoma cancer. I didn't even really know what melanoma was but the word 'cancer' was alarming. All I could think of was Tess is pregnant and just before I left for the United States we sat together in her place in Sydney playing the guitar and hanging out, laughing together.

Then Dad said she has been given less than 12 months to live! It was so much to comprehend. The call ended after that as I just needed to process it. I cried a little then headed back to my mates. Packed the tent up and said 'All is ok; Dad was just saying hi'. I was very quiet that day and they kept asking if I was ok? I said yes.

As I rode that in silence I wanted to see Tess. I asked for a sign so I knew Tess was with me and I with her. Suddenly a bird flew near me and around me, I smiled and knew that was Tess. From this point on and still today, if I think of Tess, every time, a bird will appear. Tess's spirit and presence is powerful, as even as I wrote the last sentence from this inside, I heard a bird chirp outside. This is how I know Tess is still with me! She is still part of my life.

The next day I told them what news I received and that once we reach the next town, I will end the trip, get on a bus and head to my Uncle's house (as he lived in the United States). I just had to be near some family and a telephone so I could keep up to date with any news. After I got to my uncle's house I arranged flights back to Australia.

A few weeks after returning I moved to Sydney to live with Tess, Victor and baby Mabel. I wanted to help with feeding, cooking, cleaning and be company for them all. I never wanted Tess to be alone.

All of my family did the same. Over the next month they all

relocated to Sydney from across Australia. They quit jobs. My older brother and his wife and two young kids did the same. Looking back this was a huge sacrifice by everyone! We had no plan, no jobs, no income and really no permanent places to live – but that didn't matter. It was about being there to rally around Tess and Victor.

This was a new experience for all of our family, we were learning how to personally cope as well as how to support one another. Once we all managed to have accommodation sorted across Sydney, we created a schedule of times each day and who would be doing what. Helping Victor, preparing food, looking after Mabel, time for some to rest and sleep with the priority being to never have Tess be alone and always someone around her. We had a diary in which we would document all of Tess's treatments, updated, new medicines, what to take at what time, what she would eat, etc. When one of us left Tess's company we would update the next person and hand the diary over. It was treated with this structure as we all felt responsible not to miss anything! Anything that could cause Tess to be worried or another doctor or nurse to not be 100% informed of the treatment history.

I was not in Sydney when the diagnosis was first given.

I asked family how Tess was and they said they never saw her negative. She was positive and accepting of the diagnosis of melanoma. But not of the 12 months to live diagnosis, or that it couldn't be treated. Tess was ready to do whatever it took but her priority was always her baby Mabel. She was focused on not stressing her body and being able to deliver Mabel. We didn't know if Mabel would have issues but when she was born without complications this was a relief to Tess, Victor and everyone.

The hardest part of the diagnosis for me was not being there in person. To give Tess a hug and offer my strength. I know that other family just wanted to be by her side.

I also didn't really understand Cancer or melanoma. What the different stages even meant and how she could get it? From my initial reading I kept seeing that it was about 90% caused by UV exposure, the sun. But Tess was so fair and was always so conscious to not expose her skin.

And why her? She was so young, only 30! Getting melanoma from what I thought only happened to people in their 60s or 70s after a life in the sun. Tess was only just married, had just become a mother and I kept thinking why her? Why her?

For years, Tess was single and just wanted to find love – then she did. For years she wanted to sing and act professionally, and she was now doing this.

The thought that doctors were giving her less than 12 months to live – I just kept asking how and why.

But I learned from Tess's journey how to be selfless. As the treatments didn't work and she continued to decline in health, she continued to think about others first. How we were doing and coping and how was her family (Victor and Mabel). She should have been concentrating on herself but no, this was not Tess.

I never once heard Tess question 'why me' or 'I don't deserve this'. This brings tears to my eyes as I reflect on this. Because she had every right to be angry! She should have said these things. Tess was so young, a new mother and wife and she knew (once she went into palliative care) that she would not be with us physically for much longer. But she didn't. Instead she gave strength to us all. What an 'angel', that's how my family and I describe her.

In terms of participating in clinical trials, Tess unfortunately became too sick for the drug trial that her oncologist was thinking of getting her into. It was a new anti-PD-1 drug which I later found out has had some good success in the treatment of melanoma but at the time it was brand new and not much was known about it.

What I can add is that at the time, there is just so much happening at a quick pace. I remember we were all constantly going back and forth to hospitals in Sydney. Retelling the same history over and over again to new doctors and nurses. Injections, drips, ensuring she had good food and being company. It was not all sadness and worry. Tess was taking one day a time and there were certainly times to laugh and keep the mood up in the room. Positiveness was important to us all.

In May, 2011 Tess's health declined rapidly. With no more treatment options available, the only choice left was to move Tess to palliative care, St Vincent's Hospital.

With so many in our family each day at St Vincent's, I want to say thank you to the staff. We always felt welcomed, and they certainly relaxed the visiting hours for us. Most nights several of us slept in chairs in the room with Tess and on the floor against a wall. If a room/bed was free they'd let us know. We all wanted to be close to Tess and they understood this and did all they could.

During the last precious days, we all had some quiet time with Tess. I remember this well. She kept asking how I was doing and it baffled me. Why is she concerned about me? She should think of herself, this was about her I thought? But no, Tess wanted to make sure I was ok. She told me that she was praying that I'd one day find love, it was her greatest wish for me. I think of this precious moment often and know that over the years Tess has certainly been guiding me towards finding that love she wants for me, the love she experienced with Victor and when Mabel was born.

Tess always kept hope, this really did inspire us all to do the same. Our family were raised Catholic, and praying was something we all practiced during Tess's journey. This personally gave me hope.

Tess passed away June 22, 2012. Shortly after this time I wanted to learn more about melanoma and other skin cancers and possibly see if I could help in some way. Who would have known that this decision would lead to become my focus and passion today?

When Tess passed, those that knew her contacted our family and said can they make a donation? This was all so new to us, so we researched and spoke with different organisations in the melanoma cancer research space and created a fundraising page. The page raised $12,000 and my youngest sister, Collette, and I were asked to visit them in Sydney as they wanted to say thank you.

On this occasion I met two people that would change my life. One was the Chairman of the Institute, Reg Richardson AO. A successful business man and philanthropist then in his 70s. He was so full of life and over the years has provided me with inspiration to help others as well as helping to get my later social enterprise off the ground.

The other person was Jay Allan OAM. Jay and I are still close friends today, speaking weekly and being instrumental in one another's journey since 2012.

I can't actually ever forget Jay, as he is tattooed on me! What I mean by this is we both recognise the Rocky Balboa boxing character as having resilience and never stopped going after his dreams. Jay is also a fighter, twice battled cancer but still dedicated as ever each day to supporting others through their cancer journey and finding a cure for melanoma. These gloves with a little 'J' on them are for Jay and our friendship.

## Cycling to March

I stayed in Sydney after Tess passed. And for a couple of years I volunteered at awareness events, helped at fundraisers and met a lot of people impacted by melanoma. I had a desire to do more and to bring Tess to the forefront of life again, for me, my family and all those that knew her.

I had an idea for an event. Something that would combine what I was doing when I learnt of the news (cycling) and something to raise awareness and funds for research and give hope to those impacted or experiencing melanoma. So, the idea for 'Cycling to March' was born.

So whilst working fulltime, I spent every spare moment with focus on making this happen. The plan was to start in Adelaide, then cycle through small towns making my way to Sydney to finish on the eve of a big melanoma awareness event. I was hoping the event would get some media, and share to people (impacted or not) what melanoma is, and how they can take action to prevent it via skin checks and to inform them that new advances were happening with treatment – so keep hope!

It was me, my old bike that had ridden across the United States and a map. However, over the next 12-months it snowballed with many others wanting to help, I couldn't believe it! It really does start with an idea of one person.

The event started on February 26 2014 on the steps of Adelaide Parliament house. The Lord Mayor, supporters, and a police escort guided us out of the city. Over the next 24 days, I shared this experience via social media and with newspapers, tv and radio interviews with all of Australia. I was ready to cycle 1900km on my brand new custom-built bike donated by Paul Hillbrick. Driving my support vehicles (kindly donated by Toyota) was my Mum and one of my sisters, Miriam. Mum still says it was the best experience of her life!

We were welcomed into towns and had events every day. We had countless Aussie strangers share their personal stories with us. Many even hopped on a bike and guided us out of town each morning. Media helped share our messages every day; and donations to help research flooded in. And at the centre of it all was Tess. She was the reason it was all happening, an event that allowed her name to be written and spoken again by so many; and turn the time from grieving into celebration of her life by friends and family. Many of us have and will lose loved ones in our life. We all want to remember them and I felt honoured that an idea had turned into something that offered many a chance to remember.

One highlight was receiving a letter from the (then) Prime Minster. Congratulating me on the success of Cycling to March and sharing words about Tess. Yes, this would have given Tess a smile that the leader of our country knows who she is and the impact she is still making.

The event concluded in Centennial Park with many school kids and supporters. The feeling as we crossed the line was one of immense joy and disbelief of all that had just happened. Victor and Mabel gave me a hug first and of course Jay and Reg were both there too. Jay and I still laugh about this, but he gave me a high five as I crossed the line and it caused me to wobble and nearly fall off my bike!

## Next ...

After an experience like this, it changes your life for ever. I couldn't go back to the same job or way of life. This event, the generosity so many showed and that I had experienced something amazing come from a simple idea ... I had to do more.

So in 2017 I moved back to Sunshine Coast with another idea. This time bigger than any I'd ever had. My mission was:

1.  Develop and market a new commercial product
2.  Contribute to the reduction of melanoma skin cancer:

A. by creating a preventative product solution

B. by donating to research

C. to build a brand to be part of the public awareness campaign about sun safety

This is why I created Bakslap.

## Bakslap

Bakslap came about from observation when living in Sydney. I'd surf or swim at the beach and saw countless people applying sunscreen to all areas of their body, except their back. They couldn't reach, so they leave it, exposed and at risk of being burnt. The research tells us that being burnt increases the risk of skin cancer and that the back is a high risk area.

So I understood the process of inventing, designing and manufacturing a product to solve this problem. For sunscreen and for any lotion. It was created to be a conversation starter, to encourage people to ask 'what is a bakslap'? and have the story shared – or they search and find out themselves.

The word 'Bakslap' is very Australian. We slap a mate on the back to offer congratulations or praise, to say well done. Having our brand build around this was to congratulate and praise those who practiced being sun safe and who protected themselves and their loved ones.

Most of all, creating Bakslap has allowed Tess's story to be shared with millions, both in Australia and around the world. The packaging of our lotion applicator has a beautiful illustration of an angel, Tess and her story. I've ensured our brand is full of colour and positive images.

Bakslap is leaving a legacy. Creating events and educational campaigns that share melanoma and skin cancer prevention and help raise funds to find a cure. It also allows Tess's legacy continue. For example, given Tess's love of music, we've had a song written and professionally recorded called 'I've got your back'. I never got to be in a studio with Tess when she recorded her own music but when recording this song, she was most definitely part of the entire experience with me.

All details on Bakslap and what we are involved in can be found at: www.bakslap.com.au

Today, I'm more passionate now than ever! There are so many people I work with who want to help save lives and prevent others experiencing what we have.

It's a dream in my life that a cure for melanoma is found. When it is, I know that Tess will have played a very small part towards that. She was only with us for 31 years but her selfless impact continues today. As Mabel gets older and learns from us more about her Mum, I know how proud she is!

One moment I want to share was around Father Day's 2022. It was a sign to all of us that Tess is still with us and how much she loved and appreciated family. A month before Father's Day I was back home visiting my parents. I wanted a new book to read and thought of *Les Misérables*. A famous book and also a theatre play that Tess and Dad watched and loved and it instantly became his favorite because of the memory together. Well, to my surprise, I was in the garage and happen to see Dad's copy of *Les Misérables*. I thought I'd borrow it and return it when next visiting. A few weeks later I was having a tough week and in bed a little flat, feeling the troubles in life building up. I saw the book and thought you know what, I'll start read this as it made me think of Tess and gave me a smile. I opened the book and a card fell out. I opened the card and it was a thank you card from Tess to Dad, dated 2008. Tess had written to Dad to say thank you, for supporting her in her dreams of music and acting, to being a role model and taking the time to chat with her most days. It was filled with love and immediately brought me to tears. I sent my own Father's Day gift and card to Dad, but then placed this card in an envelope with nothing on the outside.

I was not at home when Dad opened gifts that Father's Day morning, but the mood was upbeat and had laughter. Mum said (like all occasions) they placed a photo of Tess in the space where everyone gathered so she was always a part of it. Dad opened my gifts and then opened the blank envelope. Mum said he was silent and then started to cry. The card from Tess was read by everyone. Dad told me it was the greatest gift. Tess's presence made that day a greater celebration and filled the house with love and laughter as stories were shared of her.

My Mum and Dad have always been my role models in particularly regarding family and relationships. The pain and anger they must have felt that their daughter was going to pass away before them and wanting of more time together. They didn't show this, they instead showed love, thoughtfulness to one another and put all of us before themselves. They remained calm and managed the stress we kids were feeling. They too were selfless and I saw where Tess got it from.

I can only imagine the loss they feel, losing a daughter and child.

They have kept Tess's presence in their home with wonderful photos on the walls. They include her name in family cards to others and share stories of her with Mabel as she grows older.

Another moment from me is McDonalds. You might think 'how does McDonald's have anything to do with Tess?' When Tess was in palliative care and in her final week, Dad and I were out for a walk getting some food. Tess woke up and called us. She said she wanted us to pick her up some McDonalds. She felt like a Big Mac and fries. Wow, that's different, but if that's what she wants! We made sure they took care with making it and practically ran back so she had it hot. From that day on, on her birthday March 13, I always get a Big Mac meal, find a quiet place and enjoy it with Tess.

If I had any advice for people undergoing this experience, well I don't know how I would handle the initial news or journey that was ahead of me. But I would strive to be like Tess and follow her example. This is easier said than done. I'd keep positive and keep hope that the cancer will be treated, and I will get better. I'd make sure those around me are okay and be a source of strength to them.

Jay Allen

# Jay Allen OAM

I am first and foremost a devoted family man, but my experience with melanoma has given me an additional title that I am particularly proud of: The Melanoma Man.

Before we get into the nitty gritty of my own melanoma experience, let me tell you a little about myself and how I came to meet my wife, Janine, who is my rock and integral to my melanoma journey. She'll also give her perspective in some sections of my story.

## Background

I am the middle child. Fiona is my elder sister and Chantal is the youngest. I also had another younger sister, Shauna, who passed away at just 28 weeks of age. I grew up in a housing estate called Airds, located in Sydney's south west. I attended local schools – John Warby Primary and then Airds High School. When I was 11, my hard-working parents, John and Julie, bought a small four-bedroom house in a neighbouring suburb called Ambervale. It was just perfect for our little family. These younger years were so much fun and, to this day, continue to provide many happy and cherished memories.

I played rugby league my whole life and my goal was always to play in the NRL. However, after realising that I wasn't going to achieve my lifelong dream, I got my truck licence and never looked back. Life at that point was almost perfect. I had bought a house, just finished the renovations, and had two children, Jayden and Shaylee, from previous relationships. All I needed now was to find that special lady to hopefully spend the rest of my life with.

In the early summer of 2005, I was training at the gym and doing my best to generally look after myself. One of the chaps that I got to know at the gym always had an odd smell about him like some unusual skin cream or deodorant. One day, I plucked up the nerve to ask him what it was, and he responded that it was an accelerant that he used for tanning in a sunbed. He suggested that I try it, adding the words, 'The chicks dig it man.' Little did I know then that my quest for love would in fact try to kill me ...

One Saturday afternoon in early September 2006, on my way home from my weekend job delivering bread for Tip Top, I stopped off to buy a new shirt as I was going to a barbecue that night. I always wanted to look my best as you never know when you're going to meet that special someone. As I left the shopping centre carpark with the window down on my beloved Holden Commodore, I locked eyes with a petite blonde with a very pretty face. That glance was over in a second, but I immediately drove back around the carpark and right up alongside this extraordinary-looking woman. Without hesitation I said, 'Hi, how are you going?' She looked at me as she continued to walk but returned the 'Hi', albeit with an odd look on her face. I then boldly asked for her phone number. She turned around with a shocked look on her face and replied, 'That's a bit random, don't you think?' I said, 'Well I might not ever see you again,' to which she replied, 'Oh well,' and kept walking. I was so embarrassed. I slumped down in my seat and decided to leave quickly. As I was nearing the carpark exit, I glanced back about 50 metres towards this girl, and we stared at each other as I drove away. I don't know what came over me as I would never have had the nerve to do that before!

About three months later on a Sunday afternoon, my work mate Clint and I decided to head out for dinner and drinks at Bradbury pub, a popular hang out in Campbelltown (Sydney, New South Wales). However, we made a last-minute decision to go to the Catholic Club instead. Sitting inside playing the pokies,[1] I spotted this amazing-looking woman through the gap between the pokie machines. She was looking at me just as much as I was looking at her. After about half an hour of glancing at each other, my mate Clint said, 'Come on, let's play another machine.' I said, 'No way,' and gave him some more money to put in the machine as I was not leaving that spot. A drink or so later, we heard a voice say, 'Why don't you come around?' We took up the offer, of course, and I found myself in front of a familiar pretty blond and her friends. The blonde, who I only had eyes for, suddenly said, 'You don't drive a silver Commodore do you?' To this I replied, 'Yeah, why do you ask?' What followed was an embarrassing exchange of words. 'Have you ever tried to pick up a girl in the carpark at Macarthur Square shopping centre?' My mate started laughing his head off, and while I initially denied the accusation, I eventually came clean. I then asked her for her number and this time was successful! I have never really believed in fate, but that night changed my mind. I'm pleased to say that the woman from the carpark agreed to become my wife.

## Janine's perspective

As I was walking through the carpark of my local shopping centre, wearing just trackies[2] and a hoodie,[3] I spotted a silver car with what looked like a nice-looking guy driving it. I had a bit of a look and thought nothing more of it until the car drove up to me. I was quite surprised to hear a voice coming from the rather handsome man in the car asking how I was going. A little freaked out, I replied that I was good and kept walking. I was even more surprised to hear him then ask for my number. Who does that in a carpark?

The next day at work, I recall telling my friend, Jaci, how weird it was, but at the same time pondering whether I should have given my number to the handsome stranger. I decided that it was just one of those interesting little life moments and that if it was meant to be then our paths would cross again.

After spending the day at the beach for Jaci's birthday, another friend, Julz, asked us to go to the Catholic Club with her and some friends. It wasn't something I would usually do but as it was a break from the norm I went dressed very simply in a beach dress and thongs.[4] I wasn't out to impress anyone but apparently I didn't need to! Sitting in between two poker machines while my friends played, I noticed a guy opposite me. I could tell that he had noticed me too, and after a while he and his friend came around and started conversation. He looked familiar and then the penny dropped! I enquired about the type of car he drove. 'A silver Commodore,' he replied. I couldn't believe it! Who would have thought that the random guy from the carpark would one day end up being my best friend, my husband, and a father to our children? It was just meant to be.

As 2007 began, life was travelling along perfectly. I had met Janine and thought about her every minute of every waking hour. I was in love and my whole world was about this new woman in my life. I had never been so happy! Remembering the conversation about sun beds and 'chicks digging it', I went to the tanning salon repeatedly, unaware that I would end up paying the ultimate price for my vanity.

## The mole

In late 2007, a mole that had previously appeared on my left ankle seemed to be getting bigger. It was constantly itchy and scabby, and my socks would often be blood-stained, but I put it down to my work boots rubbing against it.

For over six months, Janine insisted that I get this very ugly mole checked, finally declaring that she wouldn't go on Christmas holidays with me until I had done so. I subsequently booked into my local family GP. As soon as he looked at it, he said that it needed to come off without delay. The mole was removed in early December 2007. At that stage there was no indication that it was anything other than a mole. Little did I know that melanoma was about to invade my body, and never in my wildest dreams could I have imagined what lay ahead.

## The phone call

Three days after the mole was removed, I was sitting around the backyard with friends when I received a message to call my doctor right away. It was a dreaded moment in time when you know that what follows won't be good.

---

Jay, you need to come and see me now please if you can. The mole has come back as a melanoma.

---

Janine and I jumped straight in the car and headed to the doctor's practice a mere two-minute drive away. Before taking off, we tried to reassure each other that it will be OK – it's just a skin cancer! One thing that did run through my mind during the short journey to the doctor's was the story of Clare Oliver. Clare had died of melanoma just months before at the tender age of 26, and her story had attracted significant media coverage around Australia.

## The diagnosis

My GP explained that the results were not good. He confirmed that I had a malignant melanoma measuring 1.95mm and that I would need specialist treatment in Sydney. He referred me to a melanoma specialist centre in Sydney. I just sat there as he booked me in.

Upon seeing the specialist, I learned how serious the situation was and the procedure I would have to go through. He told me that my melanoma was low grade. By his calculation this meant that if there were 100 people in a room with the same melanoma, 89 people would still be alive in five years. My interpretation of his words was that I needed surgery but that ultimately everything would be fine.

## RPA – Channel 9 medical show

The same afternoon, I received a phone call from my specialist asking if the producer of RPA, a Channel Nine medical show, could call me as they were interested in filming my journey. After discussing it with Janine, we thought it would be a good idea as we wanted to promote the danger of sun beds and the seriousness of melanoma, a silent killer.

---

To view Jay's RPA segment:
https://www.facebook.com/watch/?v=784672695050898

---

## Operation 1: Valentine's day

I was not at all apprehensive on operation day. You might say I was relatively confident that all would turn out well. Before the operation, I had to have a lymphoscintigram, a type of lymphatic mapping test, to detect how far the melanoma had spread. A special blue dye was injected into the primary mole on my left ankle. It would then travel up the leg to the lymph nodes in my groin and highlight which nodes the melanoma had travelled to if it had spread. The surgeon would then be able to track the path of the melanoma and biopsy any nodes that showed up blue. Two hours later, as I lay on the trolley waiting to go into surgery, my thoughts swayed between confidence and negativity. As for the operation, once they hit you with the big gun, you are off into a land of dreams and you can only hope.

## Recovery 1

From a distance I could hear a voice saying, 'Wake up, wake up,' along with a gentle shaking on my shoulder. As I opened my eyes, Janine was there with smile upon her face. It didn't matter to her that a film crew was taping every emotion. I spent one night in hospital.

## Janine's perspective

Despite everything Jay was going through, when he was in recovery, he still managed to arrange for me to have my own tray of hospital food for Valentine's Day. It was somewhat surprisingly delicious. I was immensely touched by this gesture. Jay had only been out of surgery for a few hours, but he was still thinking of me.

## Results day: operation 1

Walking into the hospital, I felt confident that the moment would mark the end of a 'bump' in life's journey and that I would be able to just get on with it. After being hooked up to the Channel 9 microphones, Janine and I waited for my specialist to arrive. As he entered the room, a feeling of dread washed over me, and I knew it was not going to be good.

'Unfortunately, there are a few worrying results in the pathology report,' stated the specialist.

And just like that my thoughts were in chaos and I was enveloped with overwhelming fear. My specialist told me there was a chance the melanoma may have infected other parts of my body and that I would need a total body CT scan. The more he told me, the more my fear grew.

## Janine's perspective

Hearing the specialist's words as I sat next to the man I had grown to love so much, and watching the fear come over him, made me feel sick. I looked at Jay. He had turned as white as the wall behind him. I didn't know what to do or say. While the camera crew were there with him, I ducked out to the toilet to try and gather my thoughts. My head was a mess. The next week while we waited for the CT scan was a long week that I will never forget.

## The start of the worst week of my life

On the drive home all I could think about at that moment, as I peered out the window, was why I couldn't just be a regular person doing the normal day-to-day thing. I had never been so scared in my life. As reality set in, I had no control over the tears welling in my eyes. We now had the daunting task of informing our loved ones of the outcome of the results.

Sitting in the backyard surrounded by my family, everyone was positive except me. I could not get past how something so little could be so deadly. My life was hanging in the balance. I had to put my trust in the hands of the experts. As the specialist had stated twice in our previous conversations, the chance that the melanoma had spread in my particular scenario was highly unlikely. Even though this conversation was supposed to be somewhat reassuring, it was not the answer I so wanted to hear. As any cancer patient knows, when it comes to waiting for tests and test results, the knot in your stomach gets tighter and tighter. For me, that week was like opening up the gates of hell and my now fragile mind was flooded with negative thoughts.

## The CT scan

As I lay on the CT scan table with dye pumping through my veins, I prayed that my results would be favourable. Every time the radiographer came back in to realign me I would ask, 'Have you seen anything? Is it all good?' She gave the standard response, 'I'm sorry, I'm not allowed to give out that information.' My heart was beating so fast that it felt like it was trying to escape my chest and I felt tightness restricting my breath. I was in a state of panic. At the end of the scan, I was informed that my test results would be back in the morning just before my operation.

I needed to know right away as I could not go through another night not knowing if I was going to live or die. The radiographer was informed, and Janine and I sat in the waiting room for an hour and a half, which felt like forever. The radiographer finally walked out and said, 'Everything looks fine. We cannot see any abnormalities.' That little piece of information put my world back where I wanted it to be. I then shook her hand which expanded into the biggest cuddle as an overpowering sense of relief flooded through me. I hugged Janine and, with tears welling in my eyes, sighed with relief. The RPA crew asked the radiographer if they could film the moment, but she declined as that information was for my doctor to say on camera. I remember that the producer was a little bit disappointed he could not film that moment, but such is life. I couldn't wait. The last thing on my mind was TV ratings! In saying this, the team behind the RPA series was a great support. After receiving bad results, they were my line to some form of hope. I called them and even asked at one stage what my specialist's exact words were about my diagnosis as I knew they could look back at the footage. I do not know how I would have made it through those scary days without them, to be honest. I spent a lot of time with the RPA crew, they became great friends, and I still communicate with many of them today.

## Operation 2: March 6

The RPA crew put us up for the night at the Ridges hotel just down the road from the hospital. It was a long night. I don't think I slept a minute. I knew the cancer had not spread any further than my groin, but I was still anxious as to what the operation would reveal. My operation was booked for 6:30am. Sitting in the waiting room, I must have had fear written all over me as I was terribly afraid.

## Recovery 2

As I woke up, I found myself on a ward. Janine and my daughter Shaylee were already there waiting. They had bought me a card and a 'Get Well Soon' balloon. Shaylee made me laugh, which only exacerbated the excruciating pain in my left thigh area. I was instructed not to get out of bed for five days.

I remember that first night like yesterday. Janine had just left with Shaylee, the lights were turned off, and I found myself in the cancer ward at the hospital. I could not quite believe that I was surrounded by other cancer patients. It wasn't right! I was 32-years old! I don't know what came over me but suddenly the tears and grief just took over. I was a mess for a good half an hour. I lay there crying uncontrollably. I was so scared. The week went by but each night, after Janine's departure, I was overcome with loneliness and anxiety. Every time a different doctor or nurse came into the room, I would tell them my story, wanting to know if I was going to be OK and desperate to hear the words, 'You are cured.' Unfortunately, nobody could offer me the true solace I was seeking.

## Results day: operation 2

After getting hooked up to the Channel 9 microphones again, Janine and I waited five minutes before we were called into the specialist's office. I was so nervous at the thought of what he might say. He proceeded to summarise my diagnosis and tests to date before saying, 'The pathology results show no further spread of melanoma.' So, it's all clear?' I asked, just to make sure, and he said, 'Yes.' And with that came the most indescribable feeling. A whole weight had lifted from my shoulders. I couldn't believe it. It was all gone. It could not hurt me now.

Driving home that day was awesome. It was a feeling I will never forget. I was free of cancer. In that moment, Janine and I even started to think about our wedding due to take place in a couple of months. It looked a bit shaky there for a while, but now it was full steam ahead.

## Mental anguish and life after cancer

Following the final operation, I underwent chemotherapy to reduce the risk of recurrence, and it knocked me for six. I was supposedly cured, but mentally I was not coping. I was expected to pick back up from where I left off. My parents, my friends, and everyone I met were only interested in when I was going back to work. However, it was not that simple. Being diagnosed with cancer affects your whole life – mentally, physically, and emotionally. The plan for me now was to simply get on with life, but I was terrified that the melanoma would return. In the months that followed, every time I had an ache, or a pain, I would lay there until all hours of the night wondering if it was back. Then, first thing in the morning, I would drive all the way to the hospital, about a 40-minute drive, to see one of the nurses in the melanoma unit to discuss the new pain or concern. I always received the same answers – I was worrying for nothing.

I was forever thinking that the melanoma would return. It got to the point that my thoughts were so sinister that it felt like something was eating away at my insides. My oncologist suggested I see the medical psycho-oncology counsellor, which I did. After several months, the counsellor, along with Janine, who had since become my wife, put my life back in order. They both saved me, and I simply cannot thank them enough. It took me nearly 12 months to accept that the melanoma was not going to return.

---

The one good thing that has come out of this whole journey is that I have learned that life is short and fragile. Take each day as it comes and enjoy each day. Tell the people you love the most what they mean to you.

---

## It will never be over

Every three months in the five years that followed my diagnosis, I had to return to hospital for tests to check that I remained clear of melanoma. Thirteen years on and I'm still under surveillance, albeit less often. Getting regular check-ups is a good thing. Should the melanoma return, I'll at least be on top of it. I try not to think about it, but in the days leading up to the tests, and especially on the day, I just feel so hopeless and out of control. A clear result from my doctor allows life to go back to normal until the next review scan. Staying positive is the key, although it is far easier said than done!

## My health regime

While recovering, I googled everything I could on melanoma including anti-cancer foods and holistic cancer advice. I bought the best juicer money could buy and started having healthy drinks daily. Today, I still maintain my health drinks, with carrots the principal ingredient. Rightly or wrongly, I believe that they are helping me to fight the war against recurrence. I also exercise everyday as directed by my doctor and based upon my own knowledge. There is considerable published scientific evidence on the benefits of exercise in cancer patients. I also do not drink beer anymore, but I will have the occasional red wine.

## Thoughts on life

Having looked death in the face, my experience made me realise my own mortality. The knowledge from this, as clichéd as it may sound, means that I do view things differently. Family is a gift. Thinking at the time that my days might be numbered, my thoughts turned to my children and Janine. I also wanted Janine to have a piece of me to treasure, so we agreed to try to conceive. A miracle happened and it worked! From then on, I looked at how I could turn my melanoma story into something more positive.

## Advocacy creates more battles

I joined the campaign against the use of sunbeds. I have been asked numerous times why I took on this additional battle, but if I didn't help to bring this information to the surface who would?

---

Research published in 2008 found that 281 melanomas, 43 deaths and 2,572 squamous cell carcinomas were attributable to solarium use in Australia each year at a cost to the health system of around $3 million. Read more: https://www.sunsmart.com.au/uv-radiation/solariums-and-tanning

---

My doctor was convinced my solarium use contributed to my diagnosis so I could not just sit back and do nothing. Those first 12 months sitting at home after being diagnosed gave me time to decide to do something about it. I had a truckie[5] mate whose son was great at IT and graphic design, so we had some shirts made up, created a website (sunbedban.com.au), and hit the streets! We set up awareness days, organised petitions and tried to meet with different relevant organisations.

A representative from one organisation kindly came out to my house for a cup of tea. I remember sitting in the kitchen telling the representative that we wanted to ban solariums and the response was 'Wow! That's a pretty big thing to want to achieve. I wish you luck.' I remember thinking at the time that we will conquer one day. The same organisation declined to support the campaign on the grounds that they could not publicly support a total ban. They were, however, in favour of tighter regulations. This upset me a little, but I forged ahead and eventually gained support as the years went on thanks to their policy manager. I would call to gather feedback or to ask questions about whether our ideas would gain traction. So, despite a lack of open public support, there certainly was assistance behind the scenes.

In 2010, I wrote to radio legend Alan Jones asking if he would support my campaign to ban solariums. His response was negative, and he suggested that I would have more luck in trying to ban the sun at Bondi Beach than banning solariums! I used his response as motivation to prove him wrong.

As for the politicians, I contacted almost every single one across New South Wales, asking multiple times if they would support the campaign. I made the two-hour round train trip to Parliament House in Sydney on numerous occasions to meet with someone only to be turned away. A lot of key politicians could not quite fathom why I was on a quest to ban sunbeds of all things! I would be dejected on the train ride home but would let my subconscious do its work and wake up the next day with a new idea on how to tackle this crazy industry.

The only positive response I received from emails and letters was from Federal Greens Senator Lee Rhiannon (elected 2010, resigned 2018) who agreed to meet me. I arranged a meeting as soon as possible, and from there the campaign really took off. Lee and New South Wales Greens Member of Parliament (MP) John Kaye (elected

2007, †2016) did everything in their power to support us. We held rallies in Sydney which were great! Every time we held an awareness event, I would work with my graphic design mate, Adrian, and put together a press release which we sent to all the key media outlets. Then, while on the way to an event or on the way home, I would call the radio stations asking them if they would like some news grabs about the press release. Many times, we would be driving home from an event, and I would pop up on the hourly radio news bulletin or make the 6pm news with a comment. This worked wonders for our campaign.

From my work experience at the Greens office and my encounters with Professor Simon Chapman, Lee Rhiannan and John Kay, I learnt very early on that politicians are always tuned into the media. Speaking nicely of them and mentioning them at every opportunity helps to keep items on their radar. I would frequently mention in my media comments, for example, that we looked forward to working with the State Government. Writing brief emails with a stand-out subject line is also important to avoid being placed in the cyberspace rubbish bin.

## Professor Simon Chapman

In 2011, I was privileged to meet Professor Simon Chapman, a campaign and policy legend in public health at the University of Sydney (now retired). My dad suggested I contact Simon after reading an article in a Sydney newspaper in which Simon had made a comment about the dangers of solariums. A week later, I found myself walking the vast corridors of the University of Sydney to meet with this great man. As I glanced around Simon's office, I was inspired by his achievements. I remember being a bit nervous too. Here I was, a cancer survivor from western Sydney with a degree in truck driving, about to meet a prominent advocate and academic in public health. I need not have been nervous. Once I sat down, Simon asked about my diagnosis and this became the catalyst for a very special friendship. At the end of the meeting Simon said, 'Well, I believe in you and your campaign and I'm going to help you.'

The next week we featured in The Sydney Morning Herald, one of Sydney's major newspapers, and we launched an online petition.

Momentum really started to grow from there. Simon, I, and the cancer institute then met with Frank Sartor AO who was a New South Wales minister assisting the Minister for Health (cancer). He believed in the need for a ban. I recall the meeting progressing well and provided, amongst others, a statistic relating to an even higher risk of melanoma in people under the age of 25 who use solariums. Frank then motioned his hands and said, 'Well, let's do that. Let's ban them for the under 25's as a starting point.' A few months later, new measures were announced including a solarium ban for under 25s; however, these new regulations failed to reach parliament as Frank's term as the minister came to an end before they could be passed. It was a disappointing blow at the time, but certainly not a deterrent. I pushed on.

One morning, I was interviewed live in the studio on the Channel 7 Sunrise morning TV program. To illustrate my point, I had prepared two chickens – one cooked almost burnt and the other raw. The plan was to hold these up to show what your skin looks like before and after using a solarium. The early morning interview went very well except that I totally forgot to show the chickens. I kept the idea in mind though for future use.

A key 2011 highlight of the campaign was a community cabinet meeting with the new state politicians hosted by my local western suburbs Leagues Club. I took full advantage of the opportunity and walked into the club with two chickens front and centre in a plastic bag oozing the smell of oil. One by one, community members were invited to stand up and ask their question to the key politicians lined up across the stage. I remember putting my hand up at least 25 times, but my attempts were ignored. I had the chickens ready and sitting on the outside of the bag. The smell of raw and cooked chicken wafted into the air and my hands and pants were smattered in oil. The last question opportunity of the evening was announced. I insisted on being picked by frantically putting my gooey hand in the air and mouthing to the government official, 'Please pick me!' Finally, it was my time to shine. I stood up, introduced myself and continued, 'I am a melanoma cancer survivor. My surgeon is adamant that my solarium use contributed to my diagnosis so I have started a campaign to ban them in New South Wales and I would like your help please.' I then held up the raw chicken to illustrate the skin of an 18-year-old non-solarium user, followed by the burnt chicken to mimic a solarium user. This proved to be a successful pitch as the new New South Wales Minister for Health, Jillian Skinner, asked one of her advisors to get my details and to let me know that she would be in touch. I believe that this moment was a major contributor to the solarium ban in New South Wales and I remember being so excited! Photographers were snapping away and the story with me holding the two chickens in the air made the local paper, Sydney's Daily Telegraph, and the Campbelltown newspaper's most memorable photos of the year column. A few weeks later, I met with Minister Skinner and from there things really escalated. I began to have major heartfelt meetings with very high-profile politicians including the then New South Wales Premier Barry O'Farrell, and the advisors to Prime Ministers Julia Gillard, Tony Abbot and Kevin Rudd.

## National success

Finally, in 2014, New South Wales was the first Australian state to ban solariums. I received a call from the Environment Department saying that the ban was being announced but I had to keep it quiet for a few weeks. I was driving down the Illawarra Highway at the time and had to pull over. I was so excited, and many tears were shed in that moment for all those who had sadly passed away because of these death beds.

I was determined not to miss the announcement and organised for the press conference to be held at the Poche Centre on the Mater Hospital campus in Wollstonecraft. A prominent organisation had wanted it to be held at their head office, but I was able to influence the location so that a research centre could be front and centre of the announcement. Without their support, many of the meetings in the lead up to this point would not have been possible.

After nearly a decade of largely self-funded campaigning across Australia, there was progress. One state down and a national ban to go! I continued to meet with various state health ministers. For Western Australia, I caught the 'red eye special', the famous midnight flight to Perth, and met with (at the time) Health Minister Kim Haynes. After the meeting, I was able to engage with the media. Adrian had sent out a press release and I had followed up with a phone call upon arrival, telling selected news outlets that I had arrived from New South Wales and that I was there to ban solariums. The media could not believe that I was travelling solo based on a determination to save lives. A camera crew even kindly dropped me back to the airport after the fleeting visit.

I began to understand the power of the media and my success with gaining airtime was almost synonymous with the journalist knowing my name and the reason for my call. Each time, I would silently be jumping out of my skin at a 'yes' response because all I needed was one radio interview and one TV news story to put melanoma and solariums on an individual state's radar. I was very lucky in that most times I was successful.

In Victoria, I had a momentous occasion while attending a melanoma conference. I was walking past Parliament House in Melbourne and on my way to grab some lunch with about ten melanoma mates when I noticed the then Victorian Health Minister David Davis holding a press conference on the steps. There was a strong media presence, so knowing that I had written to Minister Davis a few times and had still not received a reply, I thought I would take the opportunity right there and then to ask him why he had not responded. Without hesitation, I walked right up to the press conference surrounded by my mates and politely interrupted. I introduced myself and mentioned that I had not received a reply to my letters and emails. Minister Davis took great offence at the interruption but said he would investigate the matter before going back to his conversation. Unfortunately, this moment did not make it onto the TV screens, but I must have made some kind of an impression as a letter arrived a few weeks later.

The push to ban solariums in Victoria continued. In the lead up to the Victorian announcement, an internationally recognised medical oncologist and researcher in Melbourne Professor Grant McArthur had used my case a few times to highlight the importance of the ban. One time, he called me in the late afternoon and asked how quickly I could get to Melbourne as new regulations were being announced at 10am the next morning. I booked my flight and arrived in Melbourne at around 9pm that night ready for the next morning's solarium blitz.

The Clare Oliver campaign was no doubt the catalyst for the Victorian ban announcement. Clare died at the age of 26 in 2007 and attributed her melanoma also to solarium use. Clare bravely spoke out, and the ban that eventually followed showed that her voice did make a difference. Clare's mum, and whole medical teams across Australia, acting on a brilliant idea from the oncologist, wrote a poignant letter to the government. This carried significant weight and, together with pressure from our team and the existing ban in New South Wales, the desired goal was ultimately achieved.

The Victorian announcement to ban solariums brought a lot of tears to the many people involved in the campaign. Melissa Sheldon was one such person. She had also been a solarium user and was fighting advanced melanoma with widespread disease at the time of the announcement. She too had also put her story in the public eye to raise awareness. In 2021, at the time of writing, Melissa is completely clear of melanoma thanks to her oncologist, her wonderful medical team, and newer treatment options.

In Queensland, the 'glory' of the ban announcement itself was somewhat more political. It didn't always go as planned as the Queensland ban announcement was done very sneakily without my input. I had worked very hard in Queensland campaigning with friends. Nicole Gillespie was my good mate and a keen supporter. Tragically, she passed away in 2014 at just 32 years of age and didn't get to see the outcome of her efforts. Then two volunteers, who had lost their mum to melanoma, came on board to help with the ban. We had a great meeting with the Queensland Premier's office which I know led to the ban announcement.

I subsequently met with the Premier of Queensland in Sydney. His office had called to tell me that he would be in Sydney the next morning and wished to meet me at a designated café but to keep it quiet from the media. I was so excited, and again used my meeting to put more pressure on the Premier to outlaw solarium death machines. I felt pretty chuffed that day as the next person the Premier was meeting was a renowned surgeon Charlie Teo who had said hello on arrival but then had to wait until my meeting was over.

A few months after we had sat in the Premier's office, the two volunteers received a call from the health journalist at The Courier Mail newspaper in Brisbane saying that the announcement to ban solariums was imminent but that it was going to be released via an organisation and that I was not to take part. The night before the announcement, the health journalist called to tell me in confidence that the announcement was taking place the next morning. In other words, the organisation did not want me involved in any media and wanted it to be more about them. I was really disappointed at the time and even tried to get a late flight out of Sydney. However, once I had calmed down, I felt rather jubilant that a truck driver/solarium campaigner could have such an influence on the media that an organisation felt the need to hide it from me so they could have the attention. I looked to the positive. Solariums were now being banned in Queensland and that was what was important. I knew what the supporters and I had done to get this ban across the line and would like to especially acknowledge the efforts of Lisa Sampson.

When the bans eventually came into force, I wrote another letter to 2GB radio host Alan Jones telling him that he was wrong and that he owed me a favour one day. A devoted friend who has supported me non-stop over the years, Evelyn Field, was also instrumental in writing letters to Alan. Then, one day in 2015, the letters managed to get me into Alan's studio for an interview about the walks. I will never forget the way Alan shook my hand as if to say, 'Well done! You proved me wrong!' The radio king, like him or loath him, has supported me ever since in everything I do. I know he respects what we achieved with the ban and I greatly appreciate the enormous support we have received from Alan, Ray Hadley and radio station 2GB.

---

Solariums were finally banned on January 1, 2015 across all Australian states and territories except Western Australia (WA). Affectionately known to the locals as 'WA – wait awhile', the ban took effect the following year.

---

## Birth of The Melanoma Man

For almost a year after I was diagnosed, I was continuously in fear of my life. I would cry myself to sleep, wake up in the middle of the night in cold sweats and have bad dreams. It was an exceptionally frightening time – I will never forget it. I did not have much support other than my immediate family who did their best, but I felt a real need to talk to someone who had been diagnosed with or survived melanoma, and I was desperate for someone with accurate information to rapidly answer my questions. After my diagnosis, there was no-one for me to really connect with. It's the reason I always have time to listen to a patient now. I will do whatever I can to support a patient or a family because I know what it is like. I have been there, and it can be a very lonely and scary time in one's life without support.

Given that my story was part of the RPA program, I used to get stopped occasionally in the street and asked if I was the man with melanoma on the TV show. Then, through my early advocacy work, I became known as the Melanoma Man and the name stuck. I knew what I wanted to do but how to go about it was a bit of an initial problem. I was a truck driver who couldn't turn on a computer, didn't have an email address, and Facebook was just starting out. There was a lot to do and to learn, but I knew I wanted to take my message to the world, help as many people as possible, and create change. If I could save just one life, then it would all be worth it.

The Melanoma Man was born.

## Fundraising fuels friendships

Back in 2009, I met Phil and Dee who had featured on the TV reality program 'The Block'. Phil had been diagnosed 12 months earlier with the same stage III melanoma as I. As we could relate, meeting Phil and Dee gave Janine and I great hope. Phil and Dee introduced us to a patient-focused charity originally established in Queensland. We attended a face-to-face support meeting at the Sydney Adventist Hospital in Wahroonga, a suburb north of Sydney. This meeting was so beneficial for us – we met others who were going through the same thing, and people who had sadly lost loved ones. Little did I know that this meeting would be the start of many lifelong friendships.

Herman Herlaar led the meeting. He went on to become my best mate and was a tremendous support in the first years following my diagnosis. Herm and I would talk on the phone daily and he helped me facilitate my first support meeting here in Sydney a few months later. No matter what time I called Herm, he was always available and had the heart of a lion. Very sadly, Herman passed away to melanoma in 2014 as we were walking 900 kilometres for a cure. His last words on the phone to me a week before were to never stop supporting the people. I miss Herm so much and could not have gone on to support patients and do what I do without his guidance.

Through the Sydney support meeting, I also met Judy Middlebrook, a beautiful human who defeated stage 4 melanoma and lives in Canberra. As our friendship grew, our family would stay at her house, a small farm, and we would have an amazing time. Judy used to grow all of her own food and cook up meals equivalent to a 5-star health retreat. She has since sold her farm and is now settled in something smaller. Judy is very knowledgeable in life, and I always make sure I take her every word in. Even today, if I am worried about anything, I just call Judy. She is a wonderful mentor and friend to me.

James from Manly, a beachside Sydney suburb, and I struck up an unbreakable friendship that also evolved from the support meetings. James had sadly lost his son, Michael, 12 months earlier. Michael was just 20 years old. Before Michael passed away, James made a promise that he would do all he could to raise awareness and to fundraise for a cure. Michael loved that his dad was doing this but did not want his last name to be mentioned. It was terribly sad hearing James speak of losing his boy. James did everything possible to try to save Michael's life, including contacting many experts overseas to seek treatments that were not yet available here in Australia.

James and I speak on the phone every week and have done so for 10 years, each time trying to find new ways to raise awareness and funds for melanoma research. We will do this for the rest of our lives. For each of the three fundraising walks I have done, James has been in the background helping to connect everything and everyone – graphic designers, marketing, communications and so on. James' many contacts have helped to save us thousands in administration costs. Not only this, but James has also raised hundreds of thousands of dollars himself for melanoma research. He has never ever wanted any fuss made and just does what he does in memory of his son Michael.

---

During the walks, James would often talk about Michael's journey and we always shed many tears. One day I said to James, 'You know, you've told me this before.' And he replied, 'Yeah, I know, but you always listen.'

---

On the 1200 kilometre walk from Brisbane to Sydney, we were near the Queensland and New South Wales border and the going was tough in almost 40°C heat. I was absolutely buggered and out of water but pushed on. As it was almost lunchtime, the support cars had gone ahead to get some supplies and set up for lunch. James was walking with me for a bit as he always does and then started running ahead. He came back with some water for me, a round trip of a good couple of kilometres. This is James and what he is all about. The man is a legend and like a brother to me.

## James' story

After we lost our son in 2009, I felt I needed some kind of support. I found a melanoma support group out west in Liverpool. It was a 60-kilometre drive from where I lived in Manly. At the first meeting, I met Jay and soon realised that I was not alone. There were others struggling like me. It was a safe place where I could release my emotions and thoughts about the whole experience. I soon learnt that by talking I was also helping others who struggled with the loss of a loved one, or who were battling the disease with little hope of a cure at the time.

Whilst Michael was in palliative care, we had the most personal and confronting chats. I still feel numb when I recall my son talking about 'end of life stuff'. I think about how I told him what a great human he was, and what he had achieved for someone who had only just turned 20 years old. 'Are you preparing my eulogy?' he asked almost light heartedly. He explained that he wanted to be cremated and not have a service in a church but rather at his school where all his mates were. He did not want to lay in a cemetery where people would need to visit. To this day, we hold his ashes with us at home.

As a parent, you are supposed to go first and never have to have this kind of conversation with your own child. I mentioned to Michael that I wanted to try and make a difference by raising awareness and fundraising for a cure. He was not very keen at first to have his name mentioned and asked why I wanted to do this. I told him that if there was enough money to fund trials, and more people were vigilant about their skin, then perhaps other people and families wouldn't have to go through what he and we were going through. Michael's answer was short, 'OK, Dad.'

Jay and I are from different walks of life, but we hit it off straight away. We are both equally determined to help others and to raise awareness. Lots of ideas were tossed around for a couple of years, and in 2011 Jay and I came up with the idea of a walk. The first walk was in Manly in 2012 and the rest followed.


In 2014, together with top bloke and melanoma survivor Andrew Rust, I walked 900 kilometres from Sydney to Melbourne in 16 days and raised over $160,000 for melanoma research. After we completed this walk, I wanted more people to participate so we opened it up. One hundred and fifty people walked with me on different days of the next event which covered 1200 kilometres from Brisbane to Sydney in 29 days. It was a fantastic team effort and raised over $260,000 for melanoma research.

The next walk was even bigger – 2000 kilometres in 50 days from Adelaide to Sydney via Victoria, Canberra, and up the South Coast of New South Wales to finish at Sydney's government house where we were greeted by the Governor, Her Excellency the Honourable Margaret Beazley AC QC. Almost 300 participants helped to raise $606,000 for melanoma research during that walk.

It is truly a team effort to organise these walks with each taking 12 months of rigorous planning by a brilliant committee of volunteers, each of whom has been sadly touched by melanoma. Together, these walks have raised well over one million dollars for melanoma research. When combined with a national campaign, over 10 million dollars has been raised to date across the country.

Walking long distances day in and day out is not without pain. Your legs are tired and aching, you develop multiple blisters, and you don't necessarily have ideal walking weather. However, nothing compares to the pain of losing a loved one, or to the stories of loss from those around you. You draw inspiration and keep walking for everyone, especially those who are no longer here.

On the 2017 walk from Brisbane to Sydney, I carried a picture of James' son Michael from start to finish. When the days became tough, I would take his picture out and hold it. Michael would always give me strength. I really believe that the 61 friends I have lost to melanoma over the years are right beside me in everything I do. Some of these walks have been extremely tough, but I have smashed every one of them. I truly believe that I have had help from up above along the way. There has been a lot of work, but things have aligned along the journey that would normally seem almost impossible to achieve.

## Recognition

On January 26, 2021, I was awarded a Medal of the Order of Australia (OAM) for my commitment to skin cancer awareness. I was caught unaware by this honour and dedicated it to the many inspirational people I have met and lost due to melanoma. In 2017, I was nominated and finished amongst the top four candidates in New South Wales for the Australian of the Year awards in the local hero division. I am very humbled by this recognition, but it does not detract from the work that still needs to be done to find a cure.

## Future perspectives

The only way to get closer to a cure for melanoma is through research and more research needs to be done. More research means more options for patients and more steps towards a cure, but it doesn't come cheap. Research requires enormous amounts of money to fund the scientists, to find new treatment targets at the cellular and genome level, to create new drugs, and to test hypotheses in clinical trials. No funding means no research and I, and many close to me, have committed to raising funds for the rest of our lives.

Greg and Kay Poche deserve recognition at this point for their extraordinary efforts and philanthropy. Without mentioning their other purposeful donations, the Poche's have given well over 60 million dollars to melanoma alone, enabling the world's largest melanoma treatment centre, the Poche Centre, to open in Sydney in 2010. Greg and Kay admit to having more money through the sale of their business than they could possibly need in a lifetime and, in the spirit of the amazing humans they are, made the decision to put it to good use in Australia. There are many insanely wealthy people all over the world who could take a serious leaf out of their book.

While Covid has created practical challenges when it comes to continuing the walks, I am hopeful that there will be light at the end of this 'bump' in world history. I have several projects in mind, all focused on raising skin cancer awareness, research funding, and patient support to fill in the missing gaps.

I will not stop. This is why our new charity the Australian Skin Cancer Foundation has been born, to enable us to do what we do best, without any roadblocks!

I would like to mention the personal support my family have had from Project Dry Hire, Ricky Richards', Street Impact, HOKA Mole Map, NCIS Group Pty Ltd, and of course Toyota Australia. Thank you all so much!

Lastly I need to thank a special human being, Angela Cotroneo, a counsellor who has looked after me since 2008. When diagnosed and being as petrified as I was this amazing lady was there and still is today. I see Angela a few times each year and she always puts everything in perspective. Angela, we as a family cannot thank you enough for keeping me sane all these years. Thank you is not enough for what you have done.

---

As this book began to take shape, Jay was sadly diagnosed with stage 3 throat cancer. Not even that could deter him from his mission.

---

[1] Pokies – Australian colloquial term for gaming or slot machines often found in casinos.
[2] Trackies – Australian colloquial term for usually loose-fitting tracksuit pants or trousers.
[3] Hoodie – A hooded sweatshirt.
[4] Thongs – A casual sandal often called a flip flop in other countries.
[5] Truckie mate – Australian colloquial term for a friend who is a truck driver.

# Writing about heroes

*Aileen Eiszele - Medical Writer*

I was warned when I took this project on that it would be hard and cathartic. Initially, I brushed that thought aside. I had worked in oncology for 23 years and was used to roaming chemotherapy and radiation therapy treatment units, speaking and working with oncology specialists, attending the odd surgery or international oncology conference as part of my overall education, and being invited occasionally to talk to patients. I had witnessed a lot of oncology without being a doctor or an oncology nurse and thought that my emotions when dealing with the cancer nightmare were pretty much in check.

The warning, however, was honest and well-placed. As I sat down in my little home office late at night or on the weekend to work on each story, the tears flowed. Even my naughty little cavoodle, often curled up by my feet, would stir for a cuddle as if sensing the emotion. You can rationalise a disease like cancer taking the life of a loved one when that person has lived a full life to a ripe old age, but melanoma is a vastly different beast. This book describes the experiences of 12 women and 11 men who were, on average, 35 years old at the time of diagnosis. Of the 17 who had immunotherapy, 10 are alive at the time of writing.

I therefore found myself catapulted into the lives, or lives tragically lost, of mostly young people or those who should have been enjoying the prime of their life. Mothers who fought like hell, and who were continuing to fight, because no one else was going to raise their babies. People who miraculously won the battle and by doing so gave hope! Others who were not so fortunate but kept up the cause with immense dignity to the end despite being so incredibly unwell.

The power of people and communities brought together due to such devastating circumstances.

The ability to create change.

The strength, motivation, and determination.

The overwhelming will to simply live.

It is a tremendously humbling experience to read each story, and each brings true perspective to life's little annoying challenges.

I wish to acknowledge first and foremost the people in this book who entrusted their own story, or that of their loved one, into my care as I assisted Jay. In many cases, I know this has brought you some comfort as you continue to raise awareness and funds. For others, I also reflect on the pain and the intensely raw emotions that recounting your experience has caused.

To Jay Allen who came to me with the idea. I could not think of a better cause and I am immensely proud to have been a small part of it.

To my husband, Raphaël. I know you were initially a little sceptical, and I know this took me away from you and the children for many, many hours. To Amélie and Adrian, when you are old enough to read this book, I hope you will understand my motivation and Jay's motivation, and that you learn from each story the value and importance of life. I will hug you each more tightly.

*Aileen Eiszele is a medical writer with a background in oncology gained through professional experience in pharmaceuticals and radiation oncology in Australia and Europe. She holds a Bachelor of Arts with Honours and a Diploma of Education from the University of Tasmania and post-graduate business qualifications from Curtin University in Western Australia. She lives in Perth, is fluent in French, eats way too much chocolate, and dreams of tropical island holidays in a healthy world.*

# Definitions

*Common cancer and melanoma terminology*

## Acral lentiginous melanoma (ALM)

An uncommon melanoma subtype that appears on the palms of the hands, soles of the feet or under the nails. It often lacks the typical features of primary melanoma sometimes resulting in delayed diagnosis. Unlike cutaneous melanoma, acral melanoma is not believed to be caused by exposure to the sun or other sources of ultraviolet radiation.

## Biopsy

A biopsy is a medical procedure in which a sample of tissue (or cells) is removed from the body so that it can be examined under a microscope to aid diagnosis.

## CT scan

Computerised tomography (CT). A medical but non-invasive imaging scan that combines a series of X-ray images taken from different angles around the body.

## Cytotoxic chemotherapy

Chemotherapy, often shortened to 'chemo', is the use of drugs to treat cancer. Chemotherapy can be used with the intent to cure or to prolong life or reduce symptoms due to cancer. Chemotherapy drugs usually work by impacting a cancer cell's ability to grow and divide. Drugs can be given on their own as 'single agent' treatment, and some are used in combination with others.

## Dabrafenib

Brand name Tafinlar®. A prescription medicine manufactured by Novartis used to treat melanoma. Dabrafenib is a targeted therapy known as a signal transduction inhibitor. It blocks the activity of a mutated protein called BRAF, specifically the V600E mutated BRAF protein. This protein helps to regulate cell growth. If a BRAF mutation is present, it signals the cells to develop abnormally and to divide out of control. About half of all melanoma tumours have a BRAF mutation. The drug interferes with abnormal BRAF signals to slow stop abnormal cell growth. It is administered as an oral capsule.

### Dexamethasone

Dexamethasone is a long-acting corticosteroid drug. It has many uses in the treatment of cancer. For example, it can reduce swelling, prevent allergic reactions, assist with nausea and vomiting, stimulate appetite, and is a treatment itself for a variety of cancers.

### Immunotherapy

Immunotherapy is the use of drugs to boost the body's natural defences, or its immune system, to fight disease.

### In situ disease

The presence of abnormal cells only in the place they were first formed. They have not spread into other nearby tissues.

### Ipilimumab

Brand name Yervoy®. A prescription medicine manufactured by Bristol-Myers Squibb (BMS) used to treat melanoma. Ipilimumab is a monoclonal antibody and type of immunotherapy known as a checkpoint inhibitor. It works by blocking the activity of a molecule called CTLA-4. This molecule is a protein that prevents T cells from attacking normal body cells and cancer cells. By blocking CTLA-4, ipilimumab increases the immune system response to melanoma cells and activates T cells. It is administered as an intravenous injection.

### Leptomeningeal disease (LMD)

Leptomeningeal disease is the spread of cancer to the meninges or cerebrospinal fluid (CSF). The meninges are layers of tissue that cover and protect the brain and spinal cord like an envelope. CSF is the clear liquid found between the layers of the leptomeninges. Leptomeningeal disease tends to occur most commonly with cancers that spread to the central nervous system such as breast, lung and melanoma. Leptomeningeal metastases can affect nerves as they exit the brain and spinal cord, causing weakness and numbness. These metastases can also prevent CSF from draining properly causing CSF and pressure to build up inside the brain.

### Liquid biopsy

A liquid biopsy uses a sample of body fluids, such as blood, to look for cancer or to check on the progress of a tumour during treatment. This type of biopsy is still new, and research is ongoing to find targets in the body fluid that can be markers to indicate disease.

## Lymph nodes

Lymph nodes are part of the lymphatic system. The lymphatic system is made up of lymph vessels, lymph nodes, lymph tissue and lymph fluid. The lymphatic system is a part of the body's immune and circulatory systems. Its role is to move a colourless and watery fluid called lymph that drains from cells and tissue back into the circulatory system. By doing so, it maintains fluid levels in the body. It also absorbs fats from the digestive track, produces and releases white blood cells and other immune cells to protect the body against foreign invaders, and transports and removes waste products and abnormal cells.

Lymph nodes are bean-shaped glands that monitor and cleanse the lymph as it filters through them. There are many lymph nodes in the body, and some exist on their own while others are closely connected in groups. Some of the familiar locations of nodes are in the armpit, groin and neck. The nodes are examined in the event of a cancer diagnosis to see if they are affected. The presence of cancer in the lymph nodes is an indicator of how the cancer is spreading.

## Lymph node / sentinel node

The sentinel lymph node is the first lymph node to which cancer cells are most likely to spread from a primary tumour. A sentinel lymph node biopsy is a surgical procedure used to see if the cancer has spread to the sentinel node, that is, beyond the primary tumour site. This biopsy is performed by injecting a small amount of radioactive 'tracer' material into the primary tumour site. The tracer travels from the primary tumour to the sentinel node, taking the same pathway that any tumour cells would take. This is tracked by the radiologist and surgeon. Once found, the sentinel lymph node is surgically removed and sent to a pathologist to be examined for the presence of cancer.

## Lymphoscintigraphy

A nuclear medicine imaging technique that provides special pictures of the lymphatic system. It can be used to identify the sentinel lymph node, or the first node to receive lymph drainage from a tumour. This is useful when planning surgery.

## Medical oncologist

A specialist doctor who uses anti-cancer drug treatment to treat cancer.

## Melanoma (cutaneous melanoma)

A type of skin cancer in which the pigment-producing cells of the skin (melanocytes) become cancerous. It usually occurs on the parts of the body that have been overexposed to the sun, but not always. Australia and New

Zealand have the world's highest incidence of melanoma and melanoma is the third most common cancer diagnosed in Australia. The risk of being diagnosed with melanoma by age 85 is 1 in 13 for men compared to 1 in 21 for women.

## Melanoma stage

Cancer staging is the process of determining the amount of spread or progression of a cancer from its original site. It is one of the factors used to determine how best to treat the disease. In melanoma, there are five stages:

Stage 0: The cancer is confined to the epidermis and has not spread. This is also known as melanoma in situ.

Stage 1: The melanoma has not moved beyond the primary site and is less than 1 mm thick with or without ulceration, or 1–2 mm thick without ulceration. It has not spread.

Stage 2: The melanoma has not moved beyond the primary site and is 1–2 mm thick and ulcerated, or more than 2 mm thick with or without ulceration. It has not spread.

Stage 3: The melanoma has spread to lymph nodes near the primary site, to nearby skin or to tissues under the skin (subcutaneous).

Stage 4: There is disease outside the regional area. The melanoma has spread to distant lymph nodes or to organs such as the lungs, liver, or brain.

*Cancer staging is updated at various timepoints. This information was correct at the time of writing. Source: https://www.cancercouncil.com.au/melanoma/diagnosis/staging-prognosis accessed 231121

## Metastasis

The spread of cancer cells from the place where they first formed to another part of the body. Plural noun: metastases.

## Metastatic melanoma

Melanoma that has spread from the original lesion to other areas in the body. Also referred to as stage IV disease.

## MRI scan

Magnetic resonance imaging (MRI). A medical but non-invasive imaging scan that uses a magnetic field and radio waves to take pictures inside the body. It can produce three dimensional detailed anatomical images and is the scan of choice for soft tissues such as the brain.

## Nivolumab

Brand name Opdivo®. A prescription medicine manufactured by Bistol-Myers Squibb (BMS) used to treat melanoma. Nivolumab is monoclonal antibody and type of immunotherapy known as a checkpoint inhibitor. It promotes the tumour-killing effects of T cells (white blood cells that fight disease). It works by blocking the activity of a molecule called 'programmed cell death-1' (PD-1) which prevents T cells from recognising and attacking cancerous cells. This triggers an immune system response and activates T cells so that they can attack melanoma. It is administered as an intravenous injection.

## Oncology

A branch of medicine that deals with the prevention, diagnosis, and treatment of cancer.

## Pathology

Pathology is the study of the causes and effects of disease or injury. It is a branch of medicine that involves the study and diagnosis of disease through the examination of samples from the body such as body fluids like blood. Histopathology examines, especially under the microscope, biopsy samples, surgically removed organs, and sometimes the entire body (autopsy). The specialist doctor who performs the analysis is known as a pathologist.

## Pembrolizumab

Brand name Keytruda®. A prescription medicine manufactured by Merck used to treat melanoma. Pembrolizumab is a monoclonal antibody and a type of immunotherapy known as a checkpoint inhibitor. It works by blocking the activity of a molecule called 'programme cell death-1' (PD-1) which prevents T cells from recognising and attacking cancerous cells. This triggers an immune system response and activates T cells so that they can attack melanoma. It is administered as an intravenous injection.

## PET scan

Positron emission tomograpy (PET). A nuclear medicine imaging scan that uses a special dye containing small amounts of radioactive tracers to evaluate organ and tissue function. The most common radiotracer is F-18 fluorodeoxyglucose (FDG), a molecule similar to glucose. Cancer cells are more metabolically active and may absorb glucose at a higher rate. This higher rate can be seen on PET scans. This allows disease detection before it may be seen on other imaging tests or before it becomes symptomatic. FDG is just one of many radiotracers in use or in development. The radiotracer is usually administered as an injection.

## Prednisolone

Prednisolone is a corticosteroid drug (see 'dexamethasone'). Prednisolone is less potent that dexamethasone as an anti-inflammatory drug and is not as long acting as dexamethasone.

## Radiation oncologist

A specialist doctor who uses radiation therapy to treat cancer.

## Radiation therapy

Radiation therapy, also called radiotherapy, is a treatment that uses beams of high energy radiation directed at the tumour to damage cancer cells.

## Radiology

A branch of medicine that uses medical imaging to diagnose and treat diseases. A radiologist is a specialist doctor who interprets the images from CT, MRI, PET or ultrasound scans or X-rays. A radiographer is an allied health professional who takes the X-rays and other images.

## Response rate

A measure of the efficacy of cancer treatment is how well a patient responds to treatment. A patient's response can be measured in various ways. For example, the 'overall response rate' (ORR) refers to the percentage of people in a clinical trial or study who have a partial or complete response to treatment within a certain period of time. A complete response (CR) is the disappearance of all signs of cancer in the body. A partial response (PR) is a decrease in the size of the tumour or the amount of cancer in the body. Stable disease (SD) refers to disease that is stable – it has neither grown nor reduced. Progressive disease (PD) refers to tumours that have grown or progressed. Other measures commonly used to define the efficacy of a treatment include overall survival (OS), progression-free survival (PFS), and quality of life (QoL).

## Stereotactic body radiation therapy (SBRT)

Sometimes also referred to as stereotactic ablative radiation therapy (SABR). An advanced form of radiation therapy used to treat different types of cancer. The technique differs from other external beam radiation therapy in that it delivers higher doses of radiation in a smaller number of treatments called 'fractions'. Typically, one to five treatments are given over a few days. Treatment itself is non-invasive and not painful – there are no surgical cuts involved.

## Stereotactic radiosurgery (SRS)

Stereotactic radiosurgery is the delivery of a high focused dose of radiation therapy to a small area in the brain or other parts of the head. When one treatment is given, it is termed SRS and when more than one treatment is used it is termed stereotactic radiation therapy (SRT). Treatment is not non-invasive and not painful – there are no surgical cuts involved.

## Targeted therapy

Targeted therapy is a cancer treatment that uses drugs to target specific genes and proteins that are involved in the growth and survival of cancer cells. Targeted therapy drugs differ from cytotoxic chemotherapy drugs. Targeted therapies work on specific molecules or 'targets' involved in cancer cell growth, whereas chemotherapy drugs kill rapidly dividing normal and cancerous cells. Immunotherapy is a type of targeted therapy.

## T cell

A type of white blood cell or leukocyte, also called a T lymphocyte, that is an essential part of the immune system to fight disease.

## Trametinib

Brand name Mekinist®. A prescription medicine manufactured by Novartis. Trametinib is a signal transduction inhibitor which blocks the activity of a protein called MEK. MEK is a molecule that helps to regulate cell growth and is part of a cancer signalling pathway that includes BRAF. If there is a BRAF mutation, it signals cells, via MEK, to develop and grow abnormally. Trametinib acts on melanomas that have V600E or V600K mutations in the BRAF protein. It interferes with the abnormal BRAF signals to slow or stop abnormal cell growth. It is administered as an oral tablet.

## Vemurafenib

Brand name Zelboraf®. A prescription medicine developed by Plexxikon (now part of Daiichi-Sankyo) and Genentech for the treatment of melanoma. Vemurafenib belongs to a class of drugs called epidermal growth factor receptor (EGRF) inhibitors and is a type of targeted therapy. Vemurafenib blocks a protein molecule called BRAF which is mutated in about 50% of patients with melanoma. It is specifically indicated for patients whose tumours express the BRAF V600 mutation.

## Ultrasound scan

An ultrasound scan is a medical test that uses high-frequency sound waves outside the range of the human hearing to capture images from inside the body. This scan does not use radiation. It is also known as sonography, and the person who performs the test is a sonographer. The technology is similar to that used by sonar and radar to detect planes and ships.

Milton Keynes UK
Ingram Content Group UK Ltd.
UKHW032045180324
439698UK00003B/231

9 780648 636141